BOOKWORMS

Platinu

STORIES FOR READING CIRCLES
Stage 4 (1400 headwords)
Stage 5 (1800 headwords)

The seven short stories in this book come from different volumes in the Oxford Bookworms Library. There are five stories at Stage 4 and two stories at Stage 5. All have been specially chosen for Reading Circles.

Here are stories set in the future, and in the past; in Tibet, Australia, Paris, England, and on the planet Thalassa. There are some unusual dangers – what do you do when you get a message about the end of the universe? Or when an evil man tries to kill you with ancient magic? Or when your camels run away in the middle of the great Australian desert? There are travellers, adventurers, and lovers – happy, broken-hearted, hopeful, despairing. There are children being cruel to each other, and sometimes kind. But the first story in this book begins with one of the great mysteries of the universe . . .

OXFORD BOOKWORMS LIBRARY
Series Editor: Jennifer Bassett
Founder Editor: Tricia Hedge

~

BOOKWORMS CLUB
Platinum

STORIES FOR READING CIRCLES

Editor:
Mark Furr

OXFORD UNIVERSITY PRESS

OXFORD

UNIVERSITY PRESS

Great Clarendon Street, Oxford OX2 6DP

Oxford University Press is a department of the University of Oxford.
It furthers the University's objective of excellence in research, scholarship,
and education by publishing worldwide in

Oxford New York

Auckland Cape Town Dar es Salaam Hong Kong Karachi
Kuala Lumpur Madrid Melbourne Mexico City Nairobi
New Delhi Shanghai Taipei Toronto

With offices in

Argentina Austria Brazil Chile Czech Republic France Greece
Guatemala Hungary Italy Japan Poland Portugal Singapore
South Korea Switzerland Thailand Turkey Ukraine Vietnam

OXFORD and OXFORD ENGLISH are registered trade marks of
Oxford University Press in the UK and in certain other countries

ISBN: 978 0 19 472007 6

Printed in China

ACKNOWLEDGEMENTS

The publishers are grateful to the following for their permission to adapt and simplify
copyright texts: David Higham Associates Ltd and Scovil Chichak Galen
Literary Agency, Inc. on behalf of the estate of Arthur C. Clarke for No
Morning After, The Nine Billion Names of God, and
The Songs of Distant Earth

CONTENTS

SOURCE OF STORIES

The seven stories in this book were originally published in different volumes in the OXFORD BOOKWORMS LIBRARY. They appeared in the following titles:

No Morning After
> Arthur C. Clarke, from *The Songs of Distant Earth and Other Stories*
> Retold by Jennifer Bassett

The Nine Billion Names of God
> Arthur C. Clarke, from *The Songs of Distant Earth and Other Stories*
> Retold by Jennifer Bassett

Across the Australian Desert
> Robyn Davidson, from *Desert, Mountain, Sea*
> Retold by Sue Leather

Casting the Runes
> M. R. James, from *The Unquiet Grave*
> Retold by Peter Hawkins

The Songs of Distant Earth
> Arthur C. Clarke, from *The Songs of Distant Earth and Other Stories*
> Retold by Jennifer Bassett

Feuille d'Album
> Katherine Mansfield, from *The Garden Party and Other Stories*
> Retold by Rosalie Kerr

The Doll's House
> Katherine Mansfield, from *The Garden Party and Other Stories*
> Retold by Rosalie Kerr

~

Welcome
to Reading Circles

Reading Circles are small groups of students who meet in the classroom to talk about stories. Each student has a special role, and usually there are six roles in the Circle:

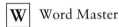 Discussion Leader 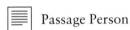 Word Master

 Summarizer  Passage Person

 Connector Culture Collector

Each role has a role sheet with notes and questions which will help you prepare for your Reading Circle discussions in the classroom. You can read more about the roles and the role sheets on pages 125 to 131 at the back of this book.

The stories in this book have been specially chosen for Reading Circles. They have many different themes, and students everywhere enjoy reading them and talking about them in their Circle. Everybody's ideas are important; there are no 'right' or 'wrong' answers when you are talking about stories.

Enjoy the reading, enjoy the talking – and discover the magic of Reading Circles . . .

Mark Furr
Hawaii, September 2008

No Morning After

~

So far we have not discovered life forms on other planets, but who knows what might be out there, light-years away from our planet Earth and our sun? And if there are other living beings somewhere, what will they be like? Will we be able to communicate with them, or they with us?

Bill Cross is a rocket engineer, who knows more about space travel than most, but this does not prepare him for the strangest message he has ever received in his life – a message from the planet Thaar five hundred light-years away . . .

ARTHUR C. CLARKE

No Morning After

Retold by Jennifer Bassett

'But this is terrible!' said the Great Scientist. 'Surely there is *something* we can do!'

'Yes, Your Highness, but it will be extremely difficult. The planet is more than five hundred light-years away, and it is hard to make contact. However, we believe we can do it, but there is another problem. So far, we have been quite unable to communicate with these people – they do not seem to be telepathic in any way. And if we cannot talk to them, we cannot help them.'

There was a long silence while the Great Scientist thought about the problem, and arrived, as he always did, at the right answer.

'Any intelligent beings must have *some* telepathic people among them. We must send out hundreds of searchers, ready to catch the smallest thought. When you find a single open mind, work as hard as you can on it. We *must* get our message through.'

'Very good, Your Highness. We will begin at once.'

Across the huge emptiness of space, which light itself took half a thousand years to cross, the brains of the planet Thaar sent out their long lines of thought, searching desperately for a single human being whose mind could receive their message. And they were lucky – they found Bill Cross.

4

At least, they thought it was luck at the time, though later they were not so sure. And it was only chance that opened Bill's mind to them for a few seconds – a chance that was not likely to happen again for many centuries.

There were three reasons for this chance happening. First, at that moment in the Earth's movement around its sun, Bill was well placed to receive a message from Thaar. So, of course, were millions of other people on the same part of the Earth's surface, but then they were not rocket engineers; they had not spent years thinking and dreaming about space and space travel.

And they were not, as Bill was, very, very drunk, on the edge of unconsciousness, trying to escape from reality into the world of dreams, where there were no disappointments.

Of course, Bill could understand the army's opinion.

'You are paid, Dr Cross,' his boss had told him sharply, 'to make rockets which can carry bombs. You are *not* paid to invent spaceships, or to use the computers here for your own purposes. So this must now stop.'

Bill knew that he wouldn't lose his job; he was too valuable to the army for that. But did he want the job anyway? He wasn't sure of anything except that he felt angry and miserable – and that Brenda had finally gone off with Johny Gardner.

He put his chin in his hands, stared dully at the white wall on the other side of the table, and emptied his mind of thought . . .

At that moment, several thousand brains on Thaar

gave a soundless cry of delight, and the wall in front of Bill disappeared into a kind of mist. He seemed to be looking down a tunnel that had no end. And in fact, he was.

Bill stared at it with interest, but he was used to seeing hallucinations when he was drunk, and he had seen more exciting ones than this. And when the voice started to speak in his mind, he did not reply at first. Even when drunk, he didn't like having conversations with himself.

'Bill,' the voice began, 'listen carefully. We have had great difficulty contacting you, and this is extremely important. We are speaking to you from a very distant planet. You are the only human being we have been able to contact, so you *must* understand what we are saying.'

Bill felt a little worried. How serious was it, he wondered, when you started to hear voices? Well, it was best not to get excited.

'OK,' he said, sounding bored. 'Go ahead and talk to me. I won't mind – if it's interesting.'

There was a pause. Then the voice continued, still in a friendly way, but now rather worried as well.

'But our message isn't just *interesting*. It means life or death for all human beings.'

'I'm listening,' said Bill. 'It'll help to pass the time.'

Five hundred light-years away, the Thaarns talked hurriedly among themselves. Something seemed to be wrong, but they could not decide exactly what. They had certainly made contact, but this was not the kind of reply they had expected. Well, they could only carry on and hope for the best.

'Listen, Bill,' they continued. 'Our scientists have just discovered that your sun is going to explode three days from now – in seventy-four hours, to be exact. Nothing can stop it. But don't be alarmed. We can save you, if you do what we say.'

'Go on,' said Bill. This hallucination was certainly unusual.

'We can make what we call a bridge – it's a kind of tunnel through space, like the one you're looking into now. It's difficult to explain, even to one of your mathematicians.'

'Just a minute,' argued Bill. 'I *am* a mathematician, and a good one, drunk or not drunk. I suppose you're talking about some kind of short cut through a higher dimension of space. That's an old idea – before Albert Einstein.'

A feeling of surprise entered Bill's mind.

'We had no idea you knew so much about science,' said the Thaarns. 'But there's no time to discuss that. The important thing is this – if you stepped into that tunnel in front of you, you'd find yourself immediately on another planet. It's a short cut, as you said, but through the thirty-seventh dimension.'

'And it leads to your world?'

'Oh no – you couldn't live here. But there are plenty of planets like Earth in the universe, and we've found one that will suit human beings. We'll make bridges like this all over Earth, so your people can just walk through them and escape. They'll have to start from the beginning on the new planet, of course, but it's their only hope. You must pass on this message, and tell them what to do.'

'But no one's going to listen to me,' Bill said. 'Why don't you talk to the president?'

'Because yours was the only mind we could contact. Others seemed closed to us; we don't understand why.'

'I could tell you,' said Bill, looking at the empty whisky bottle in front of him. He was really enjoying this hallucination, though it was easy to explain it. Only last week he'd been reading a story about the end of the world. But how good was this hallucination on details?

'If the sun does explode,' he asked, 'what will happen?'

'Your planet will be destroyed at once. All the planets, in fact, right out to Jupiter.'

Rather a fine disaster, Bill thought. And the more he thought about it, the more he liked it.

'My dear hallucination,' he said kindly, 'if I believed you—'

'But you *must* believe us!' came the worried cry across the light-years.

'I'd say *it would be a very good thing*,' Bill went on happily. 'Yes, it would save a lot of misery. No more worries about bombs, and people killing each other, or not having enough food to eat. Oh, it would be wonderful. Nice of you to come and tell us, but you can just go back home and take all your old bridges with you.'

There was great alarm and amazement on Thaar. The

Great Scientist's brain, swimming like a huge piece of rock in its bath of liquid food, turned yellow at the edges, and the main computer in the College of Higher Mathematics burnt itself out in a quarter of a second.

And on Earth, Bill Cross still hadn't finished.

'Look at *me*,' he said. 'I've spent years trying to make rockets do something useful, and they tell me I'm only allowed to make rockets for bombs, so that we can all blow each other up. The sun will make a better job of it, and if you did give us another planet, we'd only do the same stupid things all over again. And,' he went on sadly, 'Brenda's left town without even writing a note to say goodbye. So you see, I'm not very enthusiastic about your kind offer of help.'

In a final desperate attempt, the Thaarns sent their thoughts along the tunnel between the stars.

'You can't really mean it, Bill! Are *all* human beings like you?'

Bill considered this question carefully. The whisky was beginning to make him feel much happier. After all, things could be worse. Perhaps he would look for another job. As for Brenda – well, women were like buses; there'd always be another one along in a minute. And best of all, there was a second bottle of whisky in the cupboard. He got to his feet and walked drunkenly across the room to get it.

For the last time, Thaar spoke to Earth.

'Bill!' it repeated desperately. 'Surely all human beings can't be like you!'

Bill turned and looked into the misty tunnel. It seemed to have starlight shining in it, and was really rather pretty. He felt proud of himself; not many people could imagine *that*.

'Like me?' he said. 'No, they're not.' The whisky swam happily through his brain. 'I suppose I'm one of the lucky ones, really,' he said.

Then he stared in surprise, as the tunnel had suddenly disappeared and the wall was there again, exactly as it had been. Thaar knew when it was beaten.

'I was getting tired of that hallucination, anyway,' Bill thought. 'Let's see what the next one's like.'

But there wasn't a next one, because five seconds later Bill fell down unconscious, just as he was trying to open the second bottle of whisky.

For the next two days he felt rather ill and he forgot all about the strange conversation through the tunnel. On the third day he felt there was something he ought to remember, but then Brenda came back to him and there were lots of tears and kisses, and he didn't have time to think about it.

And there wasn't a fourth day, of course.

WORD FOCUS

Match each word with an appropriate meaning. Then read the report below to the Great Scientist on the planet Thaar, and use seven of the thirteen words to complete the passage. (Use one word in each gap.)

communicate	to make or think of something that is completely new
dimension	someone who studies or works in one of the sciences
drunk	the sky and everything beyond it, to the last star
hallucination	a machine that drives a spaceship up into space
invent	confused in the mind after drinking too much alcohol
light-year	being able to communicate directly from one mind to another without speaking
mathematician	an underground passage for a road or railway
planet	something which you think you see but which isn't actually there
rocket	the distance that light travels in one year
scientist	someone who studies mathematics, the science of numbers
space	Earth is one of the nine planets that move around our sun
telepathic	a measurement in space (a piece of paper has two dimensions; a box has three dimensions)
tunnel	to send information, news, ideas, etc. to other people

'Your Highness, something very strange has happened! Earth is five hundred _____ away, and it's been difficult to _____ with anyone there. Finally, we found a person called Bill who could receive our _____ messages. We told him that the Earth's sun is going to explode, and we can make a kind of _____ so that humans can take a short cut through the thirty-seventh _____ to a new _____ where they can live. Bill told us that he is a _____, and he knows a lot about science. But he seems to think it would be a good thing if his planet was destroyed . . .'

11

STORY FOCUS 1

Here are four new endings for the story. Which do you prefer? Explain why, or write a new ending for yourself.

1 The next day the Thaarns made contact with Bill again. Bill was not drunk, and he understood their message. He told the newspapers and TV stations what would happen to the sun, so the people on Earth were saved, and Bill was a hero on their new planet . . .

2 When Bill woke up, the Thaarns communicated with him again. Bill decided to go through the tunnel himself, but he did not tell anyone else on Earth about the message from Thaar. Bill was saved, but he was the only person on the new planet . . .

3 The message from Thaar was a hallucination. When Brenda came back, Bill decided to stop drinking alcohol. He and Brenda got married, and he never had another hallucination . . .

4 Later, Bill learned that the army had hidden small speakers in the ceiling of his room. The message from Thaar was not real. It was invented by the army because they wanted to frighten Bill so that he would continue to make rockets to carry bombs . . .

STORY FOCUS 2

When Bill woke up, perhaps he thought about the message from Thaar again and made a chart to help him decide what to do. Fill in the chart, with at least two reasons for each side.

PASS ON THE MESSAGE	DON'T PASS ON THE MESSAGE
1	1
2	2

The
Nine Billion
Names of God

~

People talk to God and practice their religion in many different ways. High in the mountains of Tibet, the lamas have been making a list which will contain all the possible names of God. They have been doing this work for three centuries.

But now they have come to New York to buy a computer to help them with their list, and to hire two engineers to look after the computer. So George and Chuck travel out to Tibet on the craziest job they have ever known . . .

ARTHUR C. CLARKE

The Nine Billion Names of God

Retold by Jennifer Bassett

'This is rather unusual,' said Dr Wagner, trying very hard to hide his amazement. 'I think this must be the first time that anyone has been asked to send an Automatic Sequence Computer to a monastery in Tibet. I don't wish to seem impolite, but I do wonder what use your – er – organization has for a machine like this. Could you explain just what you plan to do with it?'

'Gladly,' replied the lama, carefully putting away his little notebook. 'Your Mark 5 Computer can do all kinds of routine mathematical work which involves up to ten figures. However, for our work we are interested in *letters*, not numbers. For this reason we wish you to change the machine so that it prints out lists of words, not figures.'

'I don't quite understand . . .'

'We have been doing this work for the last three centuries – since the monastery first began, in fact. It is a little foreign to your way of thought, so I hope you will listen with an open mind while I explain it.'

'Naturally.'

'It is really quite simple. We have been making a list which will contain all the possible names of God.'

Dr Wagner's eyes opened very wide.

'We have reason to believe,' continued the lama calmly,

'that all these names can be written with not more than nine letters in an alphabet we have invented.'

'And you have been doing this for three centuries?'

'Yes. We expected it would take us about fifteen thousand years to finish the list.'

'Oh,' Dr Wagner said slowly. 'Yes, I can see why you want one of our machines. But what exactly is your *purpose* in making this list?'

The lama hesitated for a second, and Dr Wagner wondered if the question had annoyed him. But the reply came with the same calm politeness as before.

'It is a very important part of what we believe. All the many names of the Great Being – God, Allah, Jehovah, and so on – are just names invented by humans. There are certain problems in these ideas which I do not wish to discuss here. But we believe that somewhere among all the possible arrangements of letters are what we can call the *real* names of God. By going through every possible arrangement of letters, we have been trying to list them all.'

'I see. You've been starting at AAAAAAA . . . and working through to ZZZZZZZ . . .'

'Exactly – though we use a special alphabet of our own. I'm afraid it would take too long to explain all the details, as you don't understand our language.'

'I'm sure it would,' said Dr Wagner hurriedly.

'Luckily, it will be quite easy to make the necessary changes to your Automatic Sequence Computer so that it will do this work for us and print out the names. Instead of fifteen thousand years, we shall be able to finish the list in a hundred days.'

Dr Wagner could hear the sounds of the New York streets far below his office, but he felt that he was in a different world. High up in their distant, lonely mountains these lamas had been patiently at work, year after year, making their lists of meaningless words. Was there no end to the foolishness of human beings? But he must not show what he was thinking. The customer was always right . . .

'There's no doubt,' Dr Wagner said, 'that we can change the Mark 5 to print lists of this kind. I'm much more worried about the problems of making sure your computer is in good working condition when it arrives. And getting things out to Tibet, in these days, is not easy.'

'We can arrange that. The various parts of the computer are small enough to travel by air. If you can get them to India, we will collect them from there.'

'And you want to hire two of our engineers?'

'Yes, for the three months that the work should take.'

'There's no problem about that.' Dr Wagner wrote a note to remind himself. 'There are two more things . . .'

Before he could finish, the lama had passed him a piece of paper. 'This is from our bank and is signed, as you will see, by the manager.'

'Thank you,' Dr Wagner said, looking at the figures. 'That seems to be – er – adequate. The second question may seem a little strange, but sometimes these simple things get forgotten. There is electricity available . . .?'

'Yes, we brought in machinery for making electricity

about five years ago and it works very well. It's made life at the monastery much more comfortable, but the main reason for bringing it in, of course, was to have motors to drive the prayer wheels.'

'Of course,' echoed Dr Wagner. 'Why didn't I think of that?'

The view from the monastery took one's breath away at first, but in time one gets used to anything. After three months, George Hanley didn't really notice the seven-hundred-metre drop, straight down into the valley below. He was standing by the wind-smoothed stones of the low wall that ran round the outside of the main building, and staring miserably at the distant mountains. He had never been interested enough to learn their names.

This job, thought George, was the craziest thing that had ever happened to him. For weeks now the Mark 5 had been pushing out paper covered with meaningless rubbish. Patiently, endlessly, the computer had been rearranging letters in every possible way. As the sheets of paper had come out of the printers, the lamas had carefully cut them up and put them into great books. One more week, thank God, and it would be finished. George didn't know why the lamas had decided it wasn't necessary to go on to words of ten letters, or even more. His worst fear was that there would be a change of plan, and that the high lama (whom they called Sam, because it was easier than his real name) would suddenly say that the work had to go on until AD 2060.

George heard the heavy wooden door bang in the wind as Chuck came out to join him by the wall. As usual, Chuck was smoking one of the cigars that made him so popular with the lamas – who were quite willing to enjoy most of the good things in life. That was something to be thankful for, anyway. They were certainly crazy, but at least they were prepared to enjoy themselves as well.

'Listen, George,' said Chuck seriously. 'I've learned something that means trouble.'

'What's wrong? Isn't the computer behaving?' That was the worst thing that George could imagine. It might delay his return, and nothing could be more terrible than that. He wished desperately that he could be at home again.

'No, it's nothing like that.' Chuck sat on the low wall, which was unusual because normally he was frightened of the steep drop down to the valley. 'I've just learned what all this is about.'

'What d'you mean? I thought we knew.'

'Sure. We know what the lamas are trying to do. But we didn't know *why*. It's the craziest thing—'

'Tell me something new,' said George crossly.

'—but old Sam's just told me the reason. He's getting a bit excited now that we're getting close to the end of the list. You see, they believe that when they have listed all His names – and they think that there are about nine billion of them – God's purpose in making the world will be finished. There will be nothing more for human beings to do, and indeed, no further reason for humans to go on living.'

'Then what do they expect us to do?' said George. 'All go away and kill ourselves?'

'There's no need for that. When the list's completed, God steps in and simply closes everything down . . . bang!'

'Oh, I get it. When we finish our job, it will be the end of the world.'

Chuck gave a nervous little laugh. 'That's just what I said to Sam. And do you know what happened? He looked at me in a very strange way, and said, "It's nothing as small and unimportant as *that*." '

George thought about this for a moment. 'That's what I call taking the Wide View,' he said at last. 'But what do you suppose we should do about it? I don't see that it makes any difference to us. After all, we already knew that they were crazy.'

'Yes – but don't you see what may happen? When the list's complete and God doesn't ring the final bell – or whatever it is they expect – *we* may be in trouble. It's our machine they've been using. I don't like the situation one little bit.'

'Yeah,' said George slowly, 'I see what you mean. But this kind of thing's happened before, you know. When I was a child down in Louisiana, we had a crazy churchman who once said the world was going to end next Sunday. Hundreds of people believed him – even sold their homes. But when nothing happened, they didn't get angry, as you'd expect. They just decided that he'd made a mistake in his timing, and went on believing. I guess some of them still do.'

'Well, this isn't Louisiana, in case you hadn't noticed. There are just two of us and hundreds of these lamas. I like them, and I'll be sorry for old Sam when his life's work comes to nothing. But I still wish I was somewhere else.'

'I've been wishing that for weeks. But there's nothing we can do until the job's finished and the plane arrives to fly us out.'

'Of course,' said Chuck thoughtfully, 'we could always arrange for the computer to break down.'

'Not on your life! That would make things worse.'

'No, I mean like this. The machine will finish the job four days from now, and the plane calls in a week. OK – all we have to do is to find a little problem during one of our routine checks. We'll fix it, of course, but not too quickly. If we get the timing right, we can be down at the airfield when the last name comes out of the printers. They won't be able to catch us then.'

'I don't like it,' said George. 'It will be the first time I ever walked out on a job. Anyway, they might start to suspect something. No, I'll hold on and take what comes.'

'I *still* don't like it,' he said, seven days later, as the tough little mountain horses carried them down the steep road. 'And don't think I'm running away because I'm afraid. I'm just sorry for those poor old men up there, and I don't want to be around when they find out how stupid they've been. I wonder how Sam will feel about it.'

'When I said goodbye to him,' said Chuck, 'I got the

idea he knew we were walking out on him – and that he didn't care because he knew the computer was running smoothly and that the job would soon be finished. After that – well, of course, for him there just isn't any After That . . .'

George turned and stared back up the mountain road. This was the last place from which one could get a clear view of the monastery. The low, square buildings were dark against the evening sky; here and there, lights shone out from the narrow windows. What would happen, George wondered, when the list was finished? Would the lamas destroy the computer in their anger and disappointment? Or would they just sit down quietly and think out the problem all over again?

He knew exactly what was happening up on the mountain at this very moment. The high lama and his assistants were sitting quietly, looking carefully at the long sheets of paper as the younger lamas carried them away from the printers and put them into the great books. Nobody was speaking. The only sound was the endless noise of the printers as the computer did its work in complete silence. Three months of this, George thought, was enough to drive anyone mad.

'There it is!' called Chuck, looking down into the valley. 'Isn't that a beautiful sight!'

It certainly was, thought George. The small plane lay at the end of the airfield like a little silver cross. In two hours it would carry them away, back to the real, sensible world. It was a very comfortable thought.

Night falls quickly in the high Himalayas and darkness was already closing round them. Fortunately, the road was good and there was nothing dangerous about their journey at all. It was just very, very cold. The sky overhead was perfectly clear, and bright with the usual friendly stars. There would be no problem, thought George, about the pilot not being able to take off because of bad weather. That had been his only remaining worry.

He began to sing, but stopped after a while. His voice sounded rather small and lost among these great, silent mountains, shining like white ghosts on every side. They rode quietly on, and then George looked at his watch.

'We'll be there in an hour,' he called back over his shoulder to Chuck. Then he added, suddenly remembering, 'Wonder if the computer's finished the list. It should be just about now.'

Chuck didn't reply, so George turned his head to look back at him. He could just see Chuck's face, a white shape turned towards the sky.

'Look,' whispered Chuck, and George lifted his eyes to the sky. (There is always a last time for everything.)

Overhead, without any fuss, the stars were going out.

WORD FOCUS

George is unsure about leaving Tibet before the job is finished, so perhaps he uses the computer to talk online with Dr Wagner. Complete their conversation with these words.

foolish, God, lamas, monastery, rubbish, sequence, situation

GEORGE: Dr Wagner, are you there? I need to talk to you.

DR WAGNER: Hi, George, I'm here. What's the problem? Are the _____ looking after you properly?

GEORGE: Yes, they're very kind to us. They work very hard here in the _____, but they enjoy life as well.

DR WAGNER: So what's the problem then? Is it the computer?

GEORGE: No, the computer's working fine. It's printing the list of names in _____, putting them in order just as the lamas wanted. For weeks the Mark 5 has been pushing out meaningless _____.

DR WAGNER: George, we knew this was a _____ job when we sent you to Tibet. But if it's not the computer, what is it?

GEORGE: Well, today the high lama told Chuck *why* the lamas are printing out all these names. And we think this could mean trouble.

DR WAGNER: Go on.

GEORGE: The high lama said that when the list of names is finished, there will be no further reason for humans to go on living, so _____ will step in and close everything down. We're worried. When the list is complete and God *doesn't* close everything down, what will happen to us? Will they blame our computer?

DR WAGNER: Mmm. Yes, I can see you might be in a difficult _____.

GEORGE: What should we do? Chuck suggests that we try to get away just before the list is finished . . .

23

STORY FOCUS

Here are four short passages from the story. Read them and answer the questions beneath each passage.

> 'But what exactly is your *purpose* in making this list?'

1 Who says these words, to whom, and where are they at the time?
2 What answer is given to this question?

> '[The high lama] looked at me in a very strange way, and said, "It's nothing as small and unimportant as *that*."'

3 What does the *'that'* in the high lama's remark refer to?
4 What effect does the high lama's remark have on Chuck?

> 'That's what I call taking the Wide View . . . But what do you suppose we should do about it?'

5 What are George and Chuck talking about?
6 What do you think George means by 'taking the Wide View'?

> Overhead, without any fuss, the stars were going out.

7 What do you think 'without any fuss' means here?
8 How did you feel when you read this last sentence in the story?

A final challenge: Write a new, one-sentence ending for the story.

Across
the
Australian Desert

~

Some people choose to make dangerous journeys. They climb the highest mountains, dive deep into the sea, and walk across the coldest and the hottest places on earth. Why do they do it? Do they choose these journeys *because* they are difficult and dangerous?

Robyn Davidson plans to set out from Alice Springs in the middle of Australia and walk across the desert to the Indian Ocean, 2,800 kilometres away. But first she has to find some wild camels and train them to carry her supplies . . .

ROBYN DAVIDSON

Across the Australian Desert

Retold by Sue Leather

It was a beautiful Australian morning, sunny and clear. Not far from Alice Springs, in the centre of this huge country, a young woman started on a journey that would take her 2,800 kilometres across the central desert to the western coast of Australia. With her was her dog, Diggity, and four camels. It was the beginning of a very unusual adventure for the young woman, but it was also the end of many months of preparation.

1
In Alice Springs

Robyn Davidson had first arrived in Alice Springs at five o'clock one morning, over eighteen months ago, with only six dollars in her pocket. She and Diggity had travelled 800 kilometres by train from the city of Adelaide on the southern coast of Australia. Robyn wanted to walk across the central desert of Australia, from Alice Springs to the west coast, with the help of camels. She hoped to find some wild camels here in Alice and train them to carry her supplies on that long journey.

'You must be mad!' said the waitress in the cheap café where she and Diggity ate breakfast.

The woman was probably right, thought Robyn to herself. It had all seemed so different back home in Adelaide, sitting in the garden and reading books about camels. Now she was here in this hot, dusty, ugly town, with no friends and no money. All she had was a crazy idea that she wanted to walk across the desert. She felt lonely and tired after two days on the train.

'Do you know where I can find a cheap bed for the night?' she asked the waitress.

'Try the camping park three miles out of town,' the woman replied.

It was a long walk through the town. Robyn looked around at the place where she would live for some months. About 14,000 people lived in Alice Springs, and 1,000 of them were Aborigines. Most of the white people were government workers, sheep station bosses and lorry drivers. There were also some people who worked in small businesses for the tourists. The town had three pubs, a few hotels and two or three bad restaurants. Alice Springs had a lovely name, but the truth was not at all lovely, thought Robyn.

Robyn slept well that night, and woke up feeling a little happier. Now she had to find a job. Camels were expensive, and she had no money. First, she tried to find work in a pub.

'You can start in two days' time,' said the owner of the first pub she tried. 'You sleep in the back room and all meals are included.' That was perfect. She would have two days to find out about the camel businesses in town.

Camels were first brought into Australia from India and Afghanistan in the 1850s. They carried supplies during the building of the railways. There are now about 10,000 wild camels in Australia. Robyn needed just a few, and she soon learnt that there were three camel farms around Alice Springs. The next day she started her search.

'What do you know about camels?' asked the owner of the first camel farm.

'Not much.'

'And the desert?'

'Not much either but . . .'

'I don't think I can help you, miss.'

This was Sallay Mahomet, the first camel man that Robyn tried. He was a short, strong Afghan with dark eyes. His job was to bring camels from the bush and to sell them as meat to Arab countries. Robyn knew as soon as she saw him that Sallay could teach her a lot about camels, but he was not interested in helping her. Robyn carried on looking.

'I want to train some camels and take them across the desert,' she said to the next camel farmer. This one just laughed at her. Robyn realized that it *did* sound a little crazy. Perhaps she would never find anyone to teach her about camels. The only place left to try was the Posel Farm, owned by a man called Kurt Posel. 'He's a madman,' the townspeople had warned her. It was her last chance.

Kurt Posel was a tall, thin Austrian of about forty-five,

who lived at the farm with his small, gentle wife, Gladdy.
He kept camels for the tourists, who came to ride on the
animals' backs. Almost immediately, he offered Robyn a
job for eight months.

'And after that you can buy one of my camels. I'll teach
you to train camels and then you can get two wild ones as
well. You're very lucky that I'm helping you,' said Kurt, and
looked at Robyn with his ice-blue eyes.

Robyn started work at the farm immediately and also
kept her job at the pub. She was allowed to have Diggity
with her on the farm, and she felt very lucky to have found
a job so quickly.

2
The first step

Robyn woke up at 3.30 every morning. She started work
at 4.00, when she went out into the fields to catch the
camels. Her job was to bring them in and put saddles on
them. The camels spent the day taking the tourists around
the farm for a dollar a ride.

As well as this, her main jobs were to keep the yard
clean, and to feed the animals. The work was very hard
and the hours were long. But in eight months she would
have her own camels, and then her adventure could really
begin.

In the evenings she carried on working in the pub, and
slept in a small room behind it. In a letter to her family
she described her new home:

Only men drink in the pubs here, and most of them drink too much. Often they come into the pub when it opens and they don't leave until closing time, twelve hours later! One of them said to me one night, 'The Aborigines are lazy, they never want to work . . .' I just laughed to myself, because I never see these white men working. They don't like black people. And they don't like women. In fact, they dislike anybody who's different from them.

Robyn did not stay long at the pub. She did not like to hear the mens' talk, and anyway she was much too busy at the farm.

Kurt had eight camels: Biddy, Misch-Misch, Khartoum, Ali, Fahani, Aba, Bubby, and Dookie. They were all different, like human beings, Robyn thought. She liked Dookie most. He was very proud, and she thought he was like a king. She had read many books about camels, but during the next few months she learnt the truth about them. She discovered that they were intelligent (almost as intelligent as Diggity!), playful, patient, hard-working and very interesting. They could also be extremely dangerous. If they became angry, they would kick her or try to sit on her. But she loved them all and loved to watch them hour after hour.

The camels were not a problem, but Kurt was. Robyn soon began to understand why people had warned her about him. He made her work very hard, from early morning until late at night, seven days a week. When she did something wrong, he shouted at her: 'You stupid girl! Never turn your back on a camel!' He stopped her from wearing shoes, so that her feet would become harder, like a camel's. Sometimes, at the end of the day, Robyn's feet were very painful and she could not walk. But the thing that really made Robyn angry was that he was very cruel to the camels and often beat them. She hated to see him treat the animals badly.

The months went by and Robyn learnt something every day. In a strange way, Kurt's unkindness helped her, because it made her strong and fearless. But as she got stronger, Kurt became lazier and lazier, and Robyn had to work harder and harder. Some days, she felt so unhappy that she almost packed her bags and went home. Only Gladdy's kindness stopped her. 'Don't worry, love,' Gladdy used to say. 'It won't be long now.'

One day, towards the end of the eight months, Kurt came out to talk to Robyn as she was cleaning the yard.

'Tomorrow you must get up two hours earlier to bring the camels in,' he said.

Robyn felt so tired that she suddenly became very angry. 'How can you ask me to do that?' she asked. 'You're lazy. You make me do your work as well as mine!'

Kurt looked at Robyn and shouted back: 'Then you must leave!'

The next morning, Robyn packed her bags and left the farm. She felt very miserable. Now she would never get her camels. This was the end of her adventure. She knew that Kurt had made her leave the farm so that he would not have to give her the camels. He was mean, as well as lazy and cruel.

Just when Robyn was feeling that she would have to go back to Adelaide, Sallay Mahomet came back into her life. He had heard about Robyn's problems at the Posel farm, and he felt very sorry for her. 'Come and work for me for two months and I'll give you two of my wild camels,' he told her. Robyn almost kissed the old gentleman, but she decided to kiss Diggity instead. She was in business again.

During the next two months, Sallay taught her a lot about camels. She learnt how to repair saddles, how to use ropes, how to tie up a camel and many other things. Everything Robyn learnt would be extremely useful to her when she was alone in the bush. Sallay was much kinder than Kurt, too.

The day finally arrived when Sallay gave her the two camels he had promised. They were Alcoota Kate, an older, very strong camel, and Zeleika, a beautiful young one. She would have to train them, but now at last she had her own camels. As she led them off Sallay's farm one lovely Australian morning, Robyn felt very happy and very proud.

3
Camel time

Robyn went to live on a nearby farm, called Basso's Farm, with her camels – 'her girls' – and Diggity. Her plan now was to train the camels and to start her trip as soon as she could. But she still had problems.

'She's got a bad chest. You'll have to give her injections every day.' The doctor did not sound very hopeful. Robyn had asked him to come to look at Alcoota Kate, who was getting thinner and thinner and seemed to be very ill.

'Will she be all right?' Robyn asked.

'I'm not sure . . . she's very old,' the young man replied.

Kate had been used for carrying supplies some years before. She had been treated very badly and as a result she hated humans. It was therefore very difficult to get near enough to her to give her the injections she needed. Robyn tried as hard as she could.

Zeleika was thin too, but with good, regular food she seemed to get better. Zelly was a very gentle animal, and not as afraid of humans as Kate. She loved to kick though, like most camels, and Robyn was careful when she was near her. She wanted to ride Zelly, and use Kate to carry supplies.

Robyn's nearest neighbour at the farm was an Aborigine woman, Ada Baxter. She was a friendly, older woman who always called Robyn 'my daughter'. Although she had been treated badly by the white people, she did not seem to have any bad feeling towards them. She and Robyn became good friends. Robyn looked forward to meeting more Aborigines when she was travelling in the bush. She wanted to learn about them.

One day, after Robyn had been at Basso's Farm for a month, Sallay came to visit her and to have a look at the camels, who were playing in the yard.

'Zeleika is going to have a baby!' he suddenly said.

Robyn had not noticed this at all, but she believed Sallay, because he knew so much about camels. 'My God, what can I do if she has the baby on the trip?' she asked.

'Don't worry. Just tie the baby up and put it on the mother's back until it's strong enough to walk,' said Sallay. 'It won't be a problem.'

Kate, however, was becoming a real problem. She was getting sicker and sicker, and nothing seemed to help. She got so many illnesses that Robyn finally decided that she was just too old. Sallay's advice was to destroy her – to shoot her. Robyn had never killed anything before, and to kill a camel . . . to kill an animal she loved . . . she did not want to think about it. In the end, though, the camel was too ill, too much in pain. Robyn knew that she would have to do it.

When she had shot the animal through the head, Robyn cried for hours. She cried for Kate and she cried for herself. She had spent the last eighteen months here for nothing. She still only had one camel and her dream of crossing the desert seemed further away than ever before.

As usual when things looked very bad, Robyn had some good luck. Kurt Posel had sold his farm to a man who did not know how to look after camels. This man sold Robyn two bull camels, Bub and Dookie the king, for 700 dollars. She did not have the money, of course, but she was able to borrow it. Bull camels were not the best, because they were very strong and could be violent. 'But at least,' thought Robyn to herself, 'I've got three camels now.'

Zeleika, Bub and Dookie soon became very good

friends. They often went into the bush together, and sometimes it took Robyn a long time to find them. One morning, she woke up and went out into the yard as usual to see them but could not find them anywhere. They had disappeared. After searching for an hour, Robyn and Diggity found the camels' tracks, going east. They walked and walked. Finally, Diggity became too tired to walk any longer, so Robyn left her under a tree and told her to wait. Diggity did not want to wait, but she obeyed Robyn.

It was late that night when Robyn returned. Diggity, worried and thirsty, was still waiting under the tree, and did a little dance of happiness when she saw Robyn. The camels, however, were still missing.

The next day Zeleika, Bub, and Dookie had still not appeared, and some kind people from the town offered to take Robyn to look for them in their small aeroplane. Robyn was very worried. She promised herself that if she found the camels she would start her trip immediately. They flew around all day, and Robyn thought she saw the camels many times, but each time it was horses or some other animal.

Finally, as the pilot turned the plane to go back, Robyn looked round for the last time. Suddenly she saw them. Yes, it was them – the gentle Zeleika, Bub, and Dookie the king. Robyn could not believe her luck. 'I'm going to start this adventure now!' she said out loud.

4
The journey begins

Water – four big containers just for the camels, clothes, ropes, radio, cassette recorder with tapes of the Aboriginal language Pitjantjara, maps, compass, rifle, knife – these were just a few of the supplies that the camels had to carry. Then of course there was the food: bags full of oranges, potatoes, rice, tea, sugar, . . . Every day it took Robyn two hours to prepare the camels for the day's walk.

On her first night under the desert sky, Robyn had two big worries: first, losing the camels, and second, scorpions, which are small insects with a painful and dangerous bite. Fortunately, when she woke up next morning, the camels were still there and she had not been bitten by a scorpion. In fact, the main danger was from wild bull camels. 'Shoot first, and ask questions later!' Sallay had told her. This was why Robyn carried the rifle, though she hoped she would never have to use it.

It was a strange group that walked off into the desert. First came Robyn riding Bub, then came Zelly and Dookie, and finally, some metres behind, Zelly's new baby, Goliath. Diggity could be anywhere, as she usually liked to run around looking for wild rabbits. Sometimes they were lucky enough to catch a rabbit for dinner. If not, Robyn ate rice and vegetables.

She was planning to walk about thirty-two kilometres a day, six days a week, for between six and eight months, so the food she ate was very important. She had learnt about wild plants from her Aboriginal friends in Alice Springs. She knew which ones were good to eat, and as a result she became very healthy and strong.

In the evenings when the camels were unpacked, and the day's work was finished, Robyn listened to her tapes and tried to teach herself Pitjantjara. It was not easy, but she was an enthusiastic student, and hoped to speak a little of the language when she arrived in the village of Areyonga.

Areyonga was an Aboriginal village with only about ten white people. A few kilometres outside the village Robyn was met by children talking excitedly to her in Pitjantjara. When she arrived in the village, everyone came out to say hello to her, because they all thought that the *kungha ramarama* (crazy woman) could speak their language very well. This was not really true, but Robyn enjoyed trying to use the few words she knew.

Robyn stayed in Areyonga for three days with the village schoolteacher and his family. She noticed that a lot of the old Aborigines were blind, and she asked the schoolteacher about it.

'It's trachoma – a serious disease of the eye. It's one of the many illnesses the Australian Aborigines have,' he said.

'What causes it?' asked Robyn.

'Oh, bad housing, poor medical care and bad food – all caused by our government, unfortunately.'

After their rest, Robyn and the animals went on to the Tempe Downs sheep station, about sixty kilometres away.

Now the countryside became wilder and wilder, more like the desert, and Robyn began to see the tracks of wild camels on the ground. After Tempe Downs, where they collected fresh water, they went on to Ayers Rock.

Ayers Rock is a huge red rock, which rises up out of the desert sand. Robyn thought it was the most beautiful thing she had ever seen. For the Aborigines, it has a special meaning and Robyn could understand why. She camped near it, and tried to avoid the many tourists who visit it.

When she opened her eyes the next morning, she could not believe what she saw. Wild bull camels were running towards her! She quickly felt for her rifle and fired ('Shoot first, and ask questions later'). Soon there was blood everywhere; one camel was dead and the others had run off into the desert. Dookie looked afraid. Robyn was shaking with fear and anger. Shooting the wild camel had made her think of Kate again and there were tears in her eyes.

5
Mr Eddie

A few days later, Robyn and her companions arrived in the small town of Docker. Now she was in the middle of Aborigine country. The countryside was full of places, like Ayers Rock, which were special to the Aborigines. Robyn planned to go from Docker to Pipalyatjara, but she wanted to avoid the usual routes and go across the country.

'You need an old Aborigine man to go with you,' someone told her in Docker. 'Women aren't allowed to go to some of these places. You should have a guide.'

Robyn knew that this was true, so she asked the old men in the town if one of them would go with her to Pipalyatjara. They were all very polite, but the answer was 'no'. Robyn did not look forward to travelling the 250 kilometres alone, but a few days later she left Docker for Pipalyatjara.

One night, about forty kilometres from Docker, Robyn was sitting at her camp fire with Diggity when she heard the sound of a car in the distance. 'Who do you think it is, Diggity?' Diggity immediately jumped up and started barking, as she usually did when she heard a noise.

It was Aborigines – one young man and three old ones. They stayed the night and gave some of their rabbit supper to Robyn. One of the old men spoke good English and he talked and talked. Robyn liked one of the others very much. He was very small and thin and quiet. He did not speak much English, so Robyn spoke to him with her few words of Pitjantjara.

Early next morning, the men decided that one of them should go with Robyn to Pipalyatjara. She was delighted when she heard that it was going to be the small, quiet one. 'Mr Eddie,' said the man and pointed to himself. Robyn smiled at the little man. She knew that they were going to be good friends.

At first, Robyn was worried that Mr Eddie would not be able to walk thirty-two kilometres a day. He was old, and did not look very strong. In fact, he could easily walk eighty kilometres a day. Robyn also found that she no longer needed maps. Mr Eddie knew exactly where he was going. They spoke to each other in Pitjantjara. Sometimes it was difficult, but they always found something to laugh about together. They liked to laugh at the tourists with their cameras. They became good friends on the journey, and Eddie fell in love with Robyn's rifle, which he kept near to him day and night.

Two days later they arrived in Pipalyatjara, Eddie's home. Robyn knew Glendle, an official there, and she stayed with him for a few days. He told her about the work he was doing with the Aborigines.

'We have to help the Aborigines to fight for their land,' said Glendle at supper one evening. 'But the problem is that they don't think that the land really belongs to them.'

Robyn did not understand. 'What do you mean?' she asked.

'Well, for them the idea of owning land is strange – the land can own *them*, but they can't own the land.'

Robyn learnt a lot about the Aborigines in Pipalyatjara. Soon, however, it was time to go again. It was now June, and she had only completed a third of her journey. She still had the Gibson Desert ahead of her, and she wanted to get across it before the hotter weather in late September.

She asked Eddie if he would go with her to Warburton, a town 320 kilometres to the west. At first he said no, because he was 'too old', and anyway he needed new shoes. But Robyn promised to buy him some new shoes and his own rifle when they arrived in Warburton. Finally, the old man agreed, and they left.

That evening, Eddie took Robyn away from the route she had planned, because he had been born in this country and knew it very well. For a week they walked through the country, and, when they camped at night, Eddie told her many stories about the Aborigines and their customs.

They were almost at Warburton, but how much further was it exactly? Robyn asked some young Aborigines in a car. 'Little bit long way, maybe two sleeps,' they replied. It was always like this when she asked an Aborigine about distances. When she told them she was going to the sea (*uru pulka* – big lake), they said, 'Long, long way, too many sleeps that uru pulka.'

On their last night together, Eddie told Robyn that he would find her another guide after Warburton. Robyn asked him not to do this. The next part would be 640 kilometres of waterless desert – the Gibson Desert – and Robyn had decided that she wanted to go across it alone. Eddie shook his head sadly, but Robyn had made her decision.

Glendle had driven from Pipalyatjara to take Eddie home. Before Eddie left, Robyn gave him his new rifle. Eddie took it proudly, smiled at her, held her arm and shook his head. Then he got into Glendle's car and they drove off. Robyn was alone once more.

6
To the sea

Robyn wrote in her diary:

The country is dry and hot, although it is still only spring. At night and in the early morning it is quite cool, but by midday it is boiling hot again. The walking's difficult too; there's nothing but spinifex (a kind of tough, sharp grass) and sandhills. The poor camels can't find very much to eat, and are becoming thinner and thinner. Zeleika, who is feeding her baby, little Goliath, looks terribly thin. I must get to the sea before the summer starts.

Robyn had loved travelling with Eddie, but now she was happy to be alone again in the desert. She did not feel lonely because Diggity was with her. In her diary she wrote that Diggity 'is as good as a human friend, and she's a great listener'. They had a special friendship.

At Wiluna, the first real town since Alice Springs, Robyn got a muzzle for Diggity to wear round her mouth. The local farmers put poison on the ground to kill the dingos, which are Australian wild dogs. The farmers do not like dingos because they kill sheep. Robyn was afraid that her dog would eat the poison. But Diggity hated her muzzle, and looked very miserable when Robyn made her wear it. In the end, Robyn took it off, and hoped that Diggity would not go near the poison.

One night, when Robyn was resting, Diggity started

running about in a strange way. 'What's the matter, Diggity? Where've you been?' said Robyn.

The dog ran backwards and forwards. She was clearly in pain. Then she came and put her head between Robyn's legs. 'You can't be poisoned, you're my dog and you can't die,' Robyn said.

Then she remembered reading what to do in case of strychnine poisoning: 'Swing the animal around your head, in order to drive the poison out of the body.' She picked up the frightened Diggity, and began to swing her round and round her head. But she knew there was almost no chance that her dog would live. Diggity escaped from Robyn, and ran away. She was barking like a mad dog. Robyn followed her with her gun. Diggity was now in a lot of pain, and Robyn knew what she had to do. After she had killed the dog, she ran away and was violently sick.

The next morning, Robyn packed up and left the place where Diggity, her best friend, had died. She knew that she had to carry on walking.

That day, Robyn walked over fifty kilometres. Without Diggity she walked much faster. She missed her little friend very badly, and she wanted to finish the journey as quickly as possible. She now took only half an hour – not two hours – to get the camels ready every morning.

Robyn was thin, but very healthy and very brown. She usually wore very few clothes, and had not washed herself well for weeks. She felt that she looked rather strange. 'If my friends could see me now,' she told herself, 'they would think I was completely mad.'

With only 300 kilometres to go, the final disaster happened. Zeleika started bleeding very badly. She was extremely thin and Robyn was sure she would die. There was nothing to eat, and it was getting hotter every day. Robyn gave Zelly forty pills a day, hidden inside an orange. Would she be all right until they reached Dalgety, where there was a farm? Until then, Robyn tried to keep little Goliath away from his sick mother.

At Dalgety Farm, Margot and David Steadman gave poor Zelly some good food to eat. With their care the sick camel got much better. After a week at the farm Zelly had stopped bleeding and was getting a little fatter. Robyn was sure that Zelly could now manage to walk to the coast.

After their rest at Dalgety, Robyn and the camels walked on to the sea, about 200 kilometres away. It was the end of their journey. Robyn wanted to show her camels the Indian Ocean, the *uru pulka* of the Aborigines. The camels had never seen so much water before, and they became very excited. Goliath, who was still very young, ran straight into the sea for a swim; the others just ran playfully along the beach. After so much desert, it was wonderful to be near the sea. Robyn and her camels spent a week at Hamelin Pool, just resting.

Now, for the first time since she had started the journey, Robyn really thought about the future. She planned to leave the camels with some friends, Jan and David, who lived on a farm at Woodleigh, not far away. Jan and David loved camels almost as much as Robyn did, and she knew that Dookie, Bub, Zeleika, and of course Goliath, would have a good home there. But what about Robyn? For the moment, she did not know where to go or what to do. She would miss her camels and she would miss this wonderful journey. It had ended too quickly.

Robyn looked at the ocean. It was difficult to believe that she really had walked 2,800 kilometres across the desert. She thought about the people she had met who had helped her – Sallay, Gladdy, Glendle, and dear Mr Eddie. And Kurt too, in a strange kind of way. She thought sadly of Diggity, and proudly of her camels, who had survived that long, long journey. Finally, she thought about herself. She had done it, her dream had come true. She knew that wherever she went, whatever she did, her life would never be the same again.

WORD FOCUS 1

A riddle is a word puzzle. Choose words from the list to solve each riddle.

COMPASS   RIFLE
MUZZLE   ROPE
RABBIT   SADDLE

1 Shooting a wild dog? You can shoot 300 metres with this . . .
2 Riding a horse? You can put this on its back . . .
3 Am I going east, west, north, or south? This will tell me . . .
4 A dog that bites people? Put this over its mouth . . .
5 Climbing a mountain? Tie this to yourself first . . .
6 I have long ears, hop around, and live in the ground . . .

WORD FOCUS 2

Choose words from the list to complete these sentences (one word for each gap). There are two extra words which won't be needed.

aborigine, blind, bush, camels, desert, injection, muzzle, poison, saddle

1 When Robyn put the medicine through Kate's skin with a needle, she gave the camel an _____.
2 Robyn crossed a _____, which is a very hot, dry, sandy place.
3 In Australia the wild part of the country is called the _____.
4 Mr Eddie is an _____, a black person from Australia.
5 A _____ person or animal is one who is not able to see.
6 If you eat _____, it can kill you or make you very ill.
7 Robyn wanted to use _____ to help her cross the desert because they are the most suitable animals for hot, dry conditions.

Story Focus 1

Robyn is the main character in the story, but these characters are also important.

Diggity   Sallay Mahomet   Kurt Posel   Mr Eddie   Gladdy

1 Write one or two sentences about each of the characters above. Use some of these adjectives in your descriptions.
   calm, cheerful, clever, cruel, dishonest, faithful, fearless, generous, gentle, greedy, hardworking, honest, kind, lazy, mean, strong, violent
2 Which of the characters was the most helpful to Robyn? Why do you think so?
3 Which character was the least helpful? Give reasons for your answer.

Story Focus 2

Here are some extracts from Robyn's diary. Complete the extracts by choosing an adjective from the list for the first gap, and then finishing the sentences in your own words. Write as much as you like.

angry, calm, frightened, happy, lonely, lucky, relieved, sad, satisfied, strong, unhappy, weak

1 When Kurt Posel made me leave the farm, I felt _____ because

   _____.

2 When I had to shoot Alcoota Kate, I was _____ because _____.
3 I felt _____ when Mr Eddie decided to walk with me because

   _____.

4 When the bull camels ran towards me, I was _____ because

   _____.

5 After I shot Diggity, I was _____ because _____.

Casting the Runes

~

There is an old saying in English: *Sticks and stones may break my bones, but words will never hurt me*. But is that really true? Words can have great power – power to hurt, power to do evil, power to bring fear and terror to the heart.

In England, in the early 1900s, sensible men do not believe in magic or witchcraft, or in the power of ancient runes. They are just words written on a piece of paper. So why does Mr Dunning wake in the night, with terror beating in his heart, and the sense of something next to his bed, something not human . . .?

Casting the Runes

Retold by Peter Hawkins

15th April 1902
Dear Mr Karswell
I am returning your paper on 'The Truth of Alchemy',
which you have kindly offered to read at our next club
meeting. Unfortunately, we do not feel able to accept your
offer.
W. Gayton, Secretary

18th April 1902
Dear Mr Karswell
I am afraid that I am not able to arrange a meeting with
you to discuss your offer to read a paper on alchemy.
However, the club considered your offer most carefully,
and we did not refuse it until we had asked for the opinion
of an expert in these matters.
W. Gayton, Secretary

20th April 1902
The Secretary writes to inform Mr Karswell that it is
impossible for him to give the name of any person or
persons who were asked for an opinion on Mr Karswell's
paper on alchemy. The Secretary also wishes to say that he
cannot reply to any further letters on this matter.

'And who *is* Mr Karswell?' asked the Secretary's wife. She had called at his office and had just picked up and read the last of these letters.

'Well, my dear,' replied her husband, 'just at present Mr Karswell is a very angry man. All I know about him is that he's rich, lives at Lufford Abbey in Warwickshire, and considers himself to be an alchemist. And I don't want to meet him for the next week or two. Now, shall we go?'

'What have you been doing to make him angry?' asked the Secretary's wife.

'The usual thing, my dear. He sent us a paper which he wanted to read at our next meeting. We showed it to Edward Dunning – almost the only man in England who knows about these things – and he said it was no good, so we refused it. Now Karswell wants to see me about it and to find out whose opinion we asked for. Well, you've seen my reply to that. Of course, you mustn't say anything about it to anyone.'

'You know very well that I would never do a thing like that. Indeed, I hope he doesn't discover that it was poor Mr Dunning.'

'Why do you say "poor" Mr Dunning?' said the Secretary. 'He's a very happy man and quite rich, I believe. He has a comfortable home and plenty of time to spend on his hobbies.'

'I only meant that I would be sorry for him if Mr Karswell discovered his name and made trouble for him.'

'Oh yes! He would be poor Mr Dunning then,' agreed her husband.

The Secretary and his wife were lunching with friends that day, a Mr and Mrs Bennett, who came from Warwickshire. Mrs Gayton decided to ask them if they knew Mr Karswell. However, before she could do so, Mrs Bennett said to her husband:

'I saw Mr Karswell this morning. He was coming out of the British Museum as I was driving past.'

'Did you really?' said her husband. 'I wonder what brings him up to London.'

'Is he a friend of yours?' asked the Secretary, smiling at his wife.

'Oh no!' said Mr and Mrs Bennett together.

'He's one of our neighbours in Warwickshire,' explained Mrs Bennett, 'but he's not at all popular. Nobody knows what he does with his time and they say he believes in all kinds of strange and unpleasant things. If he thinks you have been impolite to him, he never forgets it, and he never does anything kind for his neighbours.'

'But, my dear,' said her husband, 'you're forgetting the Christmas party he gave for the children.'

'Oh no, I'm not,' replied his wife. 'That's a good example of what I mean.' She turned to the Secretary and his wife. 'The first winter he was at Lufford this horrible man invited all the village children to a Christmas party at his house. He said that he had some of these new moving pictures to show them. Everyone was rather surprised because they thought that he didn't like children; he used to be very angry if any of the village children came on to his land. However, the children all went and a friend of ours, Mr Farrer, went with them to see that everything was all right.'

'And was it?' asked the Secretary.

'Indeed it was not!' replied Mrs Bennett. 'Our friend said it was obvious that Mr Karswell wanted to frighten the children to death, and he very nearly did so. The first film was "Red Riding Hood", and the wolf was so terrible that several of the smaller children had to leave the room. The other films were more and more frightening. At the end Mr Karswell showed a film of a little boy in the park surrounding Lufford Abbey – every child in the room could recognize the place. There was a horrible creature in white following the little boy. At first you could see it hiding in the trees, then it became clearer and clearer and at last it caught the little boy and pulled him to pieces. Our friend said that it gave him some very bad dreams, so you can imagine how the children felt. Of course, this was too much and Mr Farrer told Karswell that he must stop it. All Mr Karswell said was: "Oh! The dear children want to go home to bed, do they? Very well, just one last picture."

'And then he showed a short film of horrible creatures with wings and lots of legs. They seemed to be crawling out of the picture to get among the children. Of course, the children were terribly frightened and they all started screaming and running out of the room. Some of them were quite badly hurt because they were all trying to get out of the room at the same time. There was the most awful trouble in the village afterwards. Several of the fathers wanted to go to Lufford Abbey and break all the windows, but the gates were locked when they got there. So you see why Mr Karswell is not one of our friends.'

'Yes,' agreed her husband. 'I think Karswell is a very dangerous man. I feel sorry for anyone who makes an enemy of him.'

'Is he the man,' asked the Secretary, 'who wrote a *History of Witchcraft* about ten years ago?'

'Yes, that's the man,' replied Mr Bennett. 'Do you remember what the newspapers said about it?'

'Yes, I do,' said the Secretary. 'They all said that it was a really bad book. In fact, I knew the man who wrote the sharpest report of them all. So did you, of course. You remember John Harrington? He was at Cambridge with us.'

'Oh, very well indeed. But I had heard nothing of him between the time we left university and the day I read about his accident in the newspaper.'

'What happened to him?' asked one of the ladies.

'It was very strange,' said Mr Bennett. 'He fell out of a tree and broke his neck. The mystery was why he had climbed the tree in the first place. There he was, an ordinary man walking home along a country road late one evening, and suddenly he began to run as fast as he could. Finally he climbed up a tree beside the road; a dead branch broke, he fell and was killed. When they found him the next morning, he had a terrible expression of fear on his face. It was quite clear that he had been chased by something and people talked about mad dogs and so on, but no one ever found the answer. That was in 1889 and ever since then his brother, Henry, who was also at Cambridge with us, has been trying to find out the truth of what happened. He thinks that someone wanted to harm his brother but, of course, he has never been able to prove anything.'

After a pause Mr Bennett asked the Secretary, 'Did you ever read Karswell's *History of Witchcraft?*'

'Yes, I did,' said the Secretary.

'And was it as bad as Harrington said?'

'Oh yes. It was badly written but what it said was very bad too, although Karswell seemed to believe every word of what he was saying.'

'I didn't read the book but I remember what Harrington wrote about it,' said Mr Bennett. 'If anyone wrote like that about one of my books, I would never write another, I'm sure.'

'I don't think Karswell feels the same way,' replied the Secretary. 'But it's half past three; we must go. Thank you for an excellent lunch.'

On the way home Mrs Gayton said, 'I hope that horrible man Karswell doesn't discover that it was Mr Dunning who said his paper was no good.'

'I don't think he's likely to do that,' replied her husband. 'Dunning won't tell him and neither shall I. The only way Karswell might find out is by asking the people at the British Museum Library for the name of anyone who studies all their old books about alchemy. Let's hope he won't think of that.'

But Mr Karswell was a very clever man.

One evening, later in the same week, Mr Edward Dunning was returning from the British Museum Library, where he had been working all day, to his comfortable home. He lived alone there, except for the two women who cooked and cleaned for him. A train took him most of the way home, then he caught a bus for the last mile or two. He had finished reading his newspaper by the time he got on the bus so he amused himself by reading the different notices on the windows opposite him. He already knew most of them quite well, but there seemed to be a new one in the corner that he had not seen before. It was yellow with blue letters, and all he could read was the name 'John Harrington'. Soon the bus was nearly empty and he changed his seat so that he could read the rest of it. It said:

REMEMBER JOHN HARRINGTON OF
THE LAURELS, ASHBROOKE, WARWICKSHIRE,
WHO DIED 18TH SEPTEMBER 1889.
HE WAS ALLOWED THREE MONTHS.

Mr Dunning stared at this notice for a long time. He was the only passenger on the bus when it reached his stop, and as he was getting off, he said to the driver, 'I was looking at that new notice on the window, the blue and yellow one. It's rather strange, isn't it?'

'Which one is that, sir?' asked the driver. 'I don't think I know it.'

'Why, this one here,' said Mr Dunning, turning to point

to it. Then he suddenly stopped – the window was now quite clear. The blue and yellow notice, with its strange message, had completely disappeared.

'But I'm sure . . .' Mr Dunning began, staring at the window. Then he turned back to the driver. 'I'm sorry. Perhaps I imagined it,' he said.

He hurried off the bus and walked home, feeling rather worried. The notice *had* been there on the window; he was sure of it. But what possible explanation could there be for its disappearing like that?

The following afternoon Mr Dunning was walking from the British Museum to the station when he saw, some way ahead of him, a man holding some leaflets, ready to give to people as they passed. However, Mr Dunning did not see him give anyone a leaflet until he himself reached the place. One was pushed into his hand as he passed. The man's hand touched his, and gave Mr Dunning an unpleasant surprise. The hand seemed unnaturally rough and hot. As Mr Dunning walked on, he looked quickly at the leaflet and noticed the name Harrington. He stopped in alarm, and felt in his pocket for his glasses, but in that second someone took the leaflet out of his hand. He turned quickly – but whoever it was had disappeared, and so had the man with the leaflets.

The next day in the British Museum he was arranging his papers on the desk when he thought he heard his own name whispered behind him. He turned round hurriedly, knocking some of his papers on to the floor, but saw no one he recognized. He picked up his papers and was beginning to work when a large man at the table behind him, who was just getting up to leave, touched him on the shoulder.

'May I give you these?' he said, holding out a number of papers. 'I think they must be yours.'

'Yes, they are mine. Thank you,' said Mr Dunning. A moment later the man had left the room.

Later, Mr Dunning asked the librarian if he knew the large man's name.

'Oh yes. That's Mr Karswell,' said the librarian. 'In fact, he asked me the other day who were the experts on alchemy, so I told him that you were the only one in the country. I'll introduce you if you like; I'm sure he'd like to meet you.'

'No, no, please don't,' said Dunning. 'He is someone I would very much prefer to avoid.'

On the way home from the museum Mr Dunning felt strangely unwell. Usually he looked forward to an evening spent alone with his books, but now he wanted to be with other people. Unfortunately, the train and the bus were unusually empty. When he reached his house, he was surprised to find the doctor waiting for him.

'I'm sorry, Dunning,' said the doctor. 'I'm afraid I've had to send both your servants to hospital.'

'Oh dear!' said Mr Dunning. 'What's the matter with them?'

'They told me they'd bought some fish for their lunch from a man who came to the door, and it has made them quite ill.'

'I'm very sorry to hear that,' said Mr Dunning.

'It's strange,' said the doctor. 'I've spoken to the neighbours and no one else has seen anyone selling fish. Now, don't worry. They're not seriously ill, but I'm afraid they won't be home for two or three days. Why don't you come and have dinner with me this evening? Eight o'clock. You know where I live.'

Mr Dunning enjoyed his evening with the doctor and returned to his lonely house at half past eleven. He had got into bed and was almost asleep when he heard quite clearly the sound of his study door opening downstairs. Alarmed, he got out of bed, went to the top of the stairs, and listened. There were no sounds of movements or footsteps, but he suddenly felt warm, even hot, air round his legs. He went back and decided to lock himself into his room, and then suddenly, the electric lights all went out. He put out his hand to find the matches on the table beside the bed – and touched a mouth, with teeth and with hair around it, and not, he said later, the mouth of a human being. In less than a second he was in another room and had locked the door. And there he spent a miserable night, in the dark, expecting every moment to hear something trying to open the door. But nothing came.

When it grew light, he went nervously back into his bedroom and searched it. Everything was in its usual place. He searched the whole house, but found nothing.

It was a miserable day for Mr Dunning. He did not want to go to the British Museum in case he met Karswell, and he did not feel comfortable in the empty house. He spent half an hour at the hospital where he found that the two women were feeling much better. Then he decided to go to the Club for lunch. There, he was very glad to find his friend the Secretary and they had lunch together. He told Gayton that his servants were in hospital, but he was unwilling to speak of his other problems.

'You poor man,' said the Secretary. 'We can't leave you alone with no one to cook your meals. You must come and stay with us. My wife and I will be delighted to have you. Go home after lunch and bring your things to my house this afternoon. No, I won't let you refuse.'

In fact, Mr Dunning was very happy to accept his friend's invitation. The idea of spending another night alone in his house was alarming him more and more.

At dinner that evening Mr Dunning looked so unwell that the Gaytons felt sorry for him and tried to make him forget his troubles. But later, when the two men were alone, Dunning became very quiet again. Suddenly he said:

'Gayton, I think that man Karswell knows that I was the person who advised you to refuse his paper.'

Gayton looked surprised. 'What makes you think that?' he asked.

So Dunning explained. 'I don't really mind,' he continued, 'but I believe that he's not a very nice person and it could be difficult if we met.'

After this Dunning sat in silence, looking more and more miserable. At last Gayton asked him if some serious trouble was worrying him.

'Oh! I'm so glad you asked,' said Dunning. 'I feel I really must talk to someone about it. Do you know anything about a man named John Harrington?'

Very surprised, Gayton could only ask why he wanted to know. Then Dunning told him the whole story of the notice in the bus, the man with the leaflets, and what had happened in his own house. He ended by asking again if Gayton knew anything about John Harrington.

Now it was the Secretary who was worried and did not quite know how to answer. His friend was clearly in a very nervous condition, and the story of Harrington's death was alarming for anyone to hear. Was it possible that Karswell was involved with both men? In the end Gayton said only that he had known Harrington at Cambridge and believed that he had died suddenly in 1889. He added a few details about the man and his books.

Later, when they were alone, the Secretary discussed the matter with his wife. Mrs Gayton said immediately that Karswell must be the link between the two men, and she wondered if Harrington's brother, Henry, could perhaps help Mr Dunning. She would ask the Bennetts where Henry Harrington lived, and then bring the two men together.

When they met, the first thing Dunning told Henry Harrington was of the strange ways in which he had learnt his brother's name. He described his other recent experiences and asked Harrington what he remembered about his brother before he died.

'John was in a very strange condition for some time before his death, it's true,' replied Henry Harrington. 'Among other things, he felt that someone was following him all the time. I'm sure that someone was trying to harm him, and your story reminds me very much of the things he experienced. Could there be any link between you and my brother, do you think?'

'Well,' replied Dunning, 'there is just one thing. I'm told that your brother wrote some very hard things about a book not long before he died and, as it happens, I too have done something to annoy the man who wrote that book.'

'Don't tell me his name is Karswell,' said Harrington.

'Why yes, it is,' replied Dunning.

Henry Harrington looked very serious.

'Well, that is the final proof I needed,' he said. 'Let me explain. I believe that my brother John was sure that this man Karswell was trying to harm him. Now, John was very fond of music. He often went to concerts in London, and always kept the concert programmes afterwards. About three months before he died, he came back from a concert and showed me the programme.

'"I nearly missed this one," he said. "I couldn't find mine at the end of the concert and was looking everywhere for it. Then my neighbour offered me his, saying that he didn't need it any more. I don't know who he was – he was a very large man."

'Soon after this my brother told me that he felt very uncomfortable at night. Then, one evening, he was looking

62

through all his concert programmes when he found something strange in the programme that his large neighbour had given him. It was a thin piece of paper with some writing on it – not normal writing. It looked to me more like Runic letters in red and black. Well, we were looking at this and wondering how to give it back to its owner when the door opened and the wind blew the paper into the fire. It was burnt in a moment.'

Mr Dunning sat silent as Harrington paused.

'Now,' he continued, 'I don't know if you ever read that book of Karswell's, *The History of Witchcraft*, which my brother said was so badly written.'

Dunning shook his head.

'Well,' Harrington went on, 'after my brother died I read some of it. The book was indeed badly written and a lot of it was rubbish, but one bit caught my eye. It was about "Casting the Runes" on people in order to harm them, and I'm sure that Karswell was writing from personal experience. I won't tell you all the details, but I'm certain that the large man at the concert was Karswell, and that the paper he gave my brother caused his death. Now, I must ask you if anything similar has happened to you.'

Dunning told him what had happened in the British Museum.

'So Karswell did actually pass you some papers?' said Harrington. 'Have you checked them? No? Well, I think we should do so at once, if you agree.'

They went round to Dunning's empty house where his

papers were lying on the table. As he picked them up, a thin piece of paper fell to the ground. A sudden wind blew it towards the open window, but Harrington closed the window just in time to stop the paper escaping. He caught the paper in his hand.

'I thought so,' he said. 'It looks just like the one my brother was given. I think you're in great danger, Dunning.'

The two men discussed the problem for a long time. The paper was covered in Runic letters which they could not understand, but both men felt certain that the message, whatever it was, could bring unknown horrors to its owner. They agreed that the paper must be returned to Karswell, and that the only safe and sure way was to give it to him in person and see that he accepted it. This would be difficult since Karswell knew what Dunning looked like.

'I can grow a beard,' said Dunning, 'so that he won't recognize me. But who knows when the end will come?'

'I think I know,' said Harrington. 'The concert where my brother was given the paper was on June 18th, and he died on September 18th, three months later.'

'Perhaps it will be the same for me,' Dunning said miserably. He looked in his diary. 'Yes, April 23rd was the day in the Museum – that brings me to July 23rd. Now, Harrington, I would very much like to know anything you can tell me about your brother's trouble.'

'The thing that worried him most,' said Harrington, 'was the feeling that whenever he was alone, someone was watching him. After a time I began to sleep in his room, and he felt better because of that. But he talked a lot in his sleep.'

'What about?' asked Dunning.

'I think it would be better not to go into details about that,' replied Harrington. 'But I remember that he received a packet by post, which contained a little diary. My brother didn't look at it, but after his death I did, and found that all the pages after September 18th had been cut out. Perhaps you wonder why he went out alone on the evening he died? The strange thing is that during the last week of his life all his worries seemed to disappear, and he no longer felt that someone was watching or following him.'

Finally, the two men made a plan. Harrington had a friend who lived near Lufford Abbey; he would stay with him and watch Karswell. If he thought they had a chance to arrange an accidental meeting, he would send a telegram to Dunning. Meanwhile, Dunning had to be ready to move at any moment and had to keep the paper safe.

Harrington went off to his friend in Warwickshire and Dunning was left alone. He found waiting very hard, and was unable to work or to take any interest in anything. He felt that he was living in a black cloud that cut him off from the world. He became more and more worried as May, June, and the first half of July passed with no word from Harrington. But all this time Karswell remained at Lufford Abbey.

At last, less than a week before July 23rd, Dunning received a telegram from his friend:

Karswell is leaving London for France on the boat train on Thursday night. Be ready. I will come to you tonight.
Harrington.

When he arrived, the two men made their final plan. The boat train from London stopped only once before Dover, at Croydon West. Harrington would get on the train in London and find where Karswell was sitting. Dunning would wait for the train at Croydon West where Harrington would look out for him. Dunning would make sure that his name was not on his luggage and, most importantly, must have the paper with him.

On Thursday night Dunning waited impatiently for the train at Croydon West. He now had a thick beard and was wearing glasses, and felt sure that Karswell would not recognize him. He noticed that he no longer felt himself to be in danger, but this only made him worry more, because he remembered what Harrington had said about his brother's last week.

At last the boat train arrived and he saw his friend at one of the windows. It was important not to show that they knew each other, so Dunning got on further down the train and slowly made his way to the right compartment.

Harrington and Karswell were alone in the compartment, and Dunning entered and sat in the corner furthest from Karswell. Karswell's heavy travelling coat and bag were on the seat opposite him, and next to where

Dunning was now sitting. Dunning thought of hiding the paper in the coat but realized that this would not do; he would have to give it to Karswell and see that Karswell accepted it. Could he hide Karswell's bag in some way, put the paper in it, and then give the bag to him as he got off the train? This was the only plan he could think of. He wished desperately that he could ask Harrington's advice.

Karswell himself seemed very restless. Twice he stood up to look out of the window. Dunning was just going to try to make his bag fall off the seat when he saw a warning expression in Harrington's eye – Karswell was watching them in the window.

Then Karswell stood up a third time, opened the window and put his head outside. As he stood up, something fell silently to the floor and Dunning saw that it was a thin wallet containing Karswell's tickets. In a moment Dunning had pushed the paper into the pocket at the back of the wallet. Just then the train began to lose speed as it came into Dover station, and Karswell closed the window and turned round.

'May I give you this, sir? I think it must be yours,' said Dunning, holding out the wallet.

'Oh, thank you, sir,' replied Karswell, checking that they were his tickets. Then he put the wallet into his pocket.

Suddenly the compartment seemed to grow dark and very hot, but already Harrington and Dunning were opening the door and getting off the train.

Dunning, unable to stand up, sat on a seat on the platform breathing deeply, while Harrington followed

Karswell the little way to the boat. He saw Karswell show his ticket to the ticket collector and pass on to the boat. As he did so, the official called after him:

'Excuse me, sir. Has your friend got a ticket?'

'What d'you mean, my friend?' shouted Karswell angrily.

'Sorry, sir. I thought there was someone with you,' apologized the ticket collector. He turned to another official beside him, 'Did he have a dog with him or something? I was sure there were two of them.'

Five minutes later there was nothing except the disappearing lights of the boat, the night wind, and the moon.

That night the two friends sat up late in their room in the hotel. Although the danger was past, a worry remained.

'Harrington,' Dunning said, 'I'm afraid we have sent a man to his death.'

'He murdered my brother,' replied Harrington, 'and he tried to murder you. It is right that he should die.'

'Don't you think we should warn him?' asked Dunning.

'How can we?' replied his friend. 'We don't know where he's going.'

'He's going to Abbeville,' said Dunning. 'I saw it on his ticket. Today is the 21st. We could send a telegram in the morning to all the main hotels in Abbeville saying: *Check your ticket wallet. Dunning.* Then he would have a whole day.'

After a pause Harrington agreed. 'I see it would make you feel happier,' he said, 'so we'll warn him.'

The telegrams were sent first thing in the morning but no one knows if Karswell received any of them. All that is known is that on July 23rd a man was looking at the front of a church in Abbeville when a large piece of stone fell from the roof and hit him on the head, killing him immediately. The police reported that nobody was on the roof at the time. From papers found on the body they discovered that the dead man was an Englishman, named Karswell.

Some months later Dunning reminded Harrington that he had never told him what his brother had talked about in his sleep. But Harrington had only said a few words when Dunning begged him to stop.

WORD FOCUS

Match each word with an appropriate meaning. Then use five of the thirteen words to complete the Secretary's diary notes about Mr Karswell.

alchemy

casting

compartment

crawl

creature

expert

horrible

leaflet

ordinary

runes

telegram

witchcraft

wolf

very frightening or unpleasant

a living being, human or non-human

someone who knows a lot about something

throwing or putting

the use of supernatural or magic powers, usually evil ones

a room on a train

a wild animal that looks like a large dog

to move slowly on hands and knees

normal, usual

an old kind of chemistry often used for witchcraft or magic

a printed piece of paper which contains information

a message sent by electrical means, then written and delivered

a very old alphabet with a mysterious or magic meaning

We decided that Mr Karswell would not read his paper about _____ at our club meeting. Edward Dunning, who is an _____ on alchemy, said that the paper was no good. Later, we also learned that Karswell did something _____ to the children in his village. He invited the children to his home and showed them some very frightening films. In the first film, the _____ was so terrible that several children had to leave the room. Another film showed a frightening _____ following a little boy, and in the end it caught the boy and tore him to pieces! Finally, we were told that the last film was even worse than this. Of course, the children were nearly frightened to death!

STORY FOCUS

After Mr Karswell died in France, perhaps the police went to his home and found some of his notes. To read Karswell's notes, match these halves of sentences to make a paragraph of seven sentences.

1 My family has studied witchcraft and alchemy for hundreds of years, . . .
2 Some people believe that I am mad or evil, . . .
3 The truth is that I need to share my deep knowledge of alchemy and witchcraft with others, . . .
4 I still feel very angry . . .
5 The man's name was Harrington, and even after he wrote those terrible things, . . .
6 Now, even though I worked for many years to write a new paper on alchemy, . . .
7 Well, once again, since Dunning has stopped me from sharing my life's work, . . .

8 . . . yet every time that I have tried to share my ideas, someone has stopped me!
9 . . . I will have to *show* him the power of the arts which I have studied all my life.
10 . . . so I am an expert in these old, magical arts.
11 . . . but I know that I am not.
12 . . . I tried to talk to him and explain my work, but he would not talk to me.
13 . . . another man, Edward Dunning, has said that my work is no good.
14 . . . when I think about the man who said terrible things about my book on witchcraft.

The Songs
of
Distant Earth

~

Humans have already walked on the surface of
the moon. One day, surely, we will build starships
that will carry us to planets millions of miles
away from Earth, young planets full of hope and
promise, where humans can begin new lives.

On the planet Thalassa, colonists from Earth
have lived untroubled lives for three hundred
years. Now Lora watches the starship Magellan
as it flies in from outer space, bringing with it
love and pain and dreams – the sweet sad songs
of distant Earth . . .

ARTHUR C. CLARKE

The Songs of Distant Earth

Retold by Jennifer Bassett

Beneath the trees Lora waited, watching the sea. She could just see Clyde's boat on the horizon, and soon it grew bigger and bigger as it came quickly over the calm blue water towards her.

'Where are you, Lora?' Clyde's voice asked crossly from the wrist radio he had given her when she agreed to marry him. 'Come and help me – we've got a lot of fish to bring home.'

So! Lora thought; *that's* why he asked me to hurry down to the beach. To punish him a little, she did not reply to his repeated calls on the radio, but when his boat arrived, she came out from the shadows under the great trees and walked slowly down the beach to meet him.

Clyde jumped out, smiling, and gave Lora a big kiss. Together, they began to empty the boat of its many kilos of fish. They were not true fish, of course; in the sea of this young planet it would be a hundred million years before nature made real fish. But they were good enough to eat, and they were called by the old names that the first colonists had brought with them from Earth.

Soon Clyde and Lora were driving the catch home, but they had made only half the short journey when the simple, carefree world they had known all their young lives came suddenly to its end.

High above them, they heard a sound their world had not known for centuries – the thin scream of a starship coming in from outer space, leaving a long white tail like smoke across the clear blue sky.

Clyde and Lora looked at each other in wonder. After three hundred years of silence, Earth had reached out once more to touch Thalassa . . .

Why? Lora asked herself. What had happened, after all these years, to bring a starship from Earth to this quiet peaceful world? There was no room for more colonists here on Thalassa, and Earth knew that well enough. It was a young planet – still only a single large island in a huge, encircling sea. In time new land would rise up out of the sea, but not for many millions of years.

When the first colonists came to Thalassa, they had worked hard to make a new life – making farms and growing food, building towns and factories. In later years, with rich farming land and seas full of fish, the colonists' descendants enjoyed an easy, comfortable life. They worked as much as necessary (but no more), happy to dream fondly of Earth, and to let the future take care of itself.

When Lora and Clyde arrived back at the village, there was great excitement. The starship, people said, seemed to be coming in to land, and it would probably come down in the hills where the first colonists had landed.

Soon everybody who could find a bicycle or a car was moving out of the village on the road to the west. Lora's father, who was the Mayor of Palm Bay village with its

572 people, proudly led the way, silently repeating to himself suitable words of welcome for the visitors.

The ship came in silently, with no sound of engines, and landed softly on the green grass. It looked, thought Lora, like a great silver egg, waiting to bring something new and strange into the peaceful world of Thalassa.

'It's so small!' someone whispered behind her. 'Did they come from Earth in *that* thing?'

'Of course not,' someone whispered back. 'That's only a little space bus. The real starship's up there in space—'

'Sshh! They're coming out!'

One moment the sides of the silver egg were smooth and unbroken; and then, a second later, there was a round doorway, with steps coming down to the ground. Then the visitors appeared, shading their eyes against the bright light of a new sun. There were seven of them – all men – tall and thin, with white faces.

They came down to the ground and Lora's father stepped forward. Words of welcome were spoken, hands were shaken, but Lora saw and heard none of it, because in that moment, she saw Leon for the first time.

He came out of the ship a little after the other seven – a man with deep, dark eyes in a strong face, eyes that had looked on sights that Lora could not even imagine. He was not handsome, and his face looked serious, even worried, but Lora knew a feeling of both fear and wonder, a feeling that her life would never be the same again.

He looked around the crowd and saw Lora. Their eyes locked together, bridging time and space and experience.

The worry slowly disappeared from Leon's face; and presently, he smiled.

It was late evening by the time all the welcoming parties had finished. Leon was very tired, but he could not sleep; his mind was still too busy with the problems of the starship. After the worry of the last few weeks, when he and the other engineers had been woken by the scream of alarm bells and had fought to save the wounded starship, it was hard to realize that they were safe at last. What luck that this planet had been so close! Now they could probably repair the ship and complete the two centuries of travelling that still lay before them. And if not, they would be able to find a new home here, among people of their own kind.

The night was cool and calm, and the sky bright with unknown stars. Still too restless to sleep, Leon left the simple resthouse that had been prepared for the visitors and walked out into the single street of Palm Bay. The villagers all seemed to be in bed and asleep, which suited Leon, who wanted only to be left alone until he felt ready to sleep.

In the quietness of the night he could hear the soft whisper of the sea, and he left the street and turned his steps towards the beach. Soon he was under the dark shadows of trees, but the smaller of Thalassa's two moons was high in the south and its thin yellow light was enough to show him the way. He came out from the trees on to the beach and stood looking at the fishing boats along the water's edge. For a moment he wished he was not a starship engineer, but could enjoy the simple, peaceful life of a fisherman on this quiet planet.

He put the dream quickly out of his mind and began to walk along by the sea's edge, and as he walked, Selene, the second moon, rose above the horizon, filling the beach with golden light.

And in that sudden brightness, Leon saw that he was not alone.

The girl was sitting on one of the boats, about fifty metres further along the beach, and staring out to sea. Leon hesitated. She was probably waiting for someone; perhaps he should turn quietly back to the village.

He had decided too late, because then the girl looked up and saw him. Unhurriedly, she rose to her feet, and Leon walked slowly on towards her. He stopped a few metres away from her and smiled.

'Hello,' he said. 'I was just taking a late walk – I hope I haven't frightened you.'

'Of course not,' Lora answered, trying to keep her voice calm and expressionless. She could not really believe that she was doing this – meeting a complete stranger on a lonely beach at night. All day she had been unable to put the young engineer out of her mind. She had found out his name, had watched and planned, and hurried to the beach ahead of him when she saw him leave the resthouse and walk towards the trees. Now she felt suddenly afraid, but it was too late to turn back.

Leon began to speak again, then stopped, suddenly

recognizing her and realizing what she was doing here. This was the girl who had smiled at him when he came out of the ship – no, that was not right; *he* had smiled at *her* . . .

They stared at each other wordlessly, wondering what strange chance of time and space had brought them together.

This is crazy, Leon told himself. What am I doing here? I should apologize and go – and leave this girl to the peaceful world that she has always known.

But he did not leave. 'What's your name?' he said.

'I'm Lora,' she answered, in the soft voice of the islanders.

'And I'm Leon Carrell, Assistant Rocket Engineer, Starship *Magellan*.'

She smiled a little and he saw at once that she already knew his name. Then she spoke again:

'How long do you think you will be here, on Thalassa?'

'I'm not sure,' he replied, truthfully enough. He could see that his answer was important to her. 'It depends how long it takes to do our repairs. We have to make a new starship shield, you see, as the old one was destroyed when something big hit us out in space.'

'And you think you can make a new one here?'

'We hope so. The main problem is how to lift about a million tonnes of water up to the *Magellan*.'

'Water?' Lora looked puzzled. 'I don't understand.'

'Well, you know that a starship travels through space at

79

almost the speed of light. Unfortunately, space is full of bits and pieces of rock and other things, and at that speed anything that hits us would burn up the ship immediately. So we carry a shield about a kilometre ahead of us, and let *that* get burned up instead.'

'And you can make a new one out of *water*?'

'Yes. It's the cheapest building material in the universe. We freeze it into a huge piece of ice that travels ahead of us. What could be simpler than that?'

Lora did not answer, and seemed to be thinking of something else. Presently she said, a little sadly:

'And you left Earth a hundred years ago.'

'A hundred and four. It seems like only a few weeks because we were deep-sleeping until the alarms woke us engineers. The ship is flown by automatic controls, of course, and all the other colonists are still in suspended animation. They don't know that anything has happened.'

'And soon you'll join them again, and sleep your way on to the stars for another two hundred years.'

'That's right,' said Leon, not looking at her.

Lora looked round at the island behind them. 'It's strange to think that your sleeping friends up there will never know anything of all this. I feel sorry for them.'

'Yes, only we fifty engineers will remember Thalassa.' He looked at Lora's face and saw sadness in her eyes. 'Why does that make you unhappy?'

Lora shook her head, unable to answer. She felt a great loneliness, a horror at the huge emptiness of space and that three-hundred-year journey through the emptiness. Suddenly she wanted to be at home, in her own room, in the world she knew and understood. She wished she had never come on this mad adventure – and she thought of Clyde, and felt ashamed.

'What's the matter?' asked Leon. 'Are you cold?' He held out his hand to her and their fingers touched, but she pulled her hand away at once.

'It's late,' she said, almost angrily. 'I must go home. Goodbye.'

She turned and walked quickly away, leaving Leon staring after her, puzzled and a little hurt. What had he said to annoy her? Then he called after her:

'Will I see you again?'

If she answered, the words were lost in the noise of the sea, but Leon knew, as surely as the sun would rise tomorrow, that they would meet again.

The life of the island now centred around the huge wounded starship two thousand kilometres out in space. In the early morning and late evening, the *Magellan* could be seen as a bright star in the sky above. And even when it could not be seen, people were thinking and talking about it. It was the most exciting thing that had happened to Thalassa in centuries.

The starship's engineers seemed to be busy all the time, hurrying around the island, digging deep holes in the ground to study the rocks, using strange scientific tools that the islanders had never seen before. Most people, in fact, had no idea at all what the engineers were doing, and the engineers, although friendly, had no time to explain.

It was two days before Lora spoke to Leon again. From time to time she saw him as he hurried around the village, but they were only able to smile at each other in passing. But this was enough to make Lora's heart beat wildly, and to make her sharp and unfriendly with Clyde. She had been so sure that she loved Clyde, and would marry him. Now she was not sure of anything, except her desperate, burning wish to be with Leon every minute of the day. Why this had happened to her, she did not know. She knew only that she had fallen in love with a man who had come into her life from nowhere, and who must leave again in a few weeks.

By the end of the first day, only her family knew about her feelings; by the end of the second day, everyone she passed gave her a knowing smile. It was impossible in a small place like Palm Bay to keep anything secret.

Her second meeting with Leon was in the Mayor's office. Lora was helping her father with the paperwork that the Earthmen's visit had caused when the door opened and Leon walked in, asking to see the Mayor. Lora's younger sister hurried away to fetch him, and Leon sat tiredly down in a chair by the door. Then he saw Lora watching him silently from the other side of the room, and jumped to his feet.

'Hello – I didn't know you worked here.'

'I live here. My father's the Mayor.'

Leon walked over to her desk and picked up a book

that was lying there. He said something about it and Lora replied politely, but there were unspoken questions in her mind. When can we meet again? And does he really like me, or is he just making polite conversation?

Then the Mayor hurried in to see his visitor, who had brought a message from the starship's captain. Lora pretended to work but she understood not one word of the papers she was reading.

When Leon had left, the Mayor walked over to his daughter and picked up some of the papers on her desk.

'He seems a nice young man,' he said, 'but is it a good idea to get too fond of him?'

'I don't know what you mean,' said Lora.

'Now, Lora! I *am* your father, and I do have *eyes* in my head, you know.'

'He's not' – and here Lora's voice shook a little – 'a bit interested in me.'

'Are you interested in him?'

'I don't know. Oh, Daddy, I'm so unhappy!'

The Mayor was not a brave man, so there was only one thing he could do. He gave Lora his handkerchief, and ran back into his office.

It was the most difficult problem that Clyde had ever had in his life. Lora belonged to him – everyone knew that. With another villager, or a man from any other part of Thalassa, Clyde knew exactly what he would do. And because Clyde was a tall, strong young man, there had never been any trouble at those other times when he had politely advised the man to leave his girl alone. But Leon was an Earthman, an important visitor. It was not easy to offer that kind of advice to him, however politely.

During his long hours at sea, Clyde played with the idea of a short, sharp fight with Leon. But he knew that he was stronger than the Earthman, so it wouldn't be a fair fight.

And anyway, was he really sure that he had a reason to fight Leon? It was true that Leon seemed to be at the Mayor's house every time that Clyde called, but that could mean everything – or nothing. Jealousy was new to Clyde, and he did not like it at all.

He was still very angry indeed about the dance. It had been the biggest, grandest party for years – with the President of Thalassa, all the important people on the island, and fifty visitors from Earth, all at the same time.

Clyde was a good dancer, but he had little chance to show it that night. Leon had been showing everyone the latest dances from Earth (well, from a hundred years before, anyway) and in Clyde's opinion the dances were ugly and Leon was an awful dancer. He had been foolish enough to tell Lora that during one of their few dances together, and that had been his last dance with Lora that evening. From that moment on Lora neither looked at nor spoke to him, and Clyde had soon gone off to the bar to get drunk as quickly as possible. In this he was successful, and it was only the next morning that he learnt what he had missed.

The dancing had ended early. Then the President

introduced the captain of the starship, who, he said, had a little surprise for everyone.

Captain Gold spoke for a short while first. He wanted, he said, to thank Thalassa for its warm welcome to the visitors from Earth. He spoke of the peace and beauty of the island, and the kindness of its people. He hoped that he and his companions would make the world that was waiting at the end of their journey as happy a home for human beings as Thalassa was. Then he went on:

'Much has happened on Earth in the three centuries since the first colonists came to Thalassa, and this is one way in which we can show our thanks to you. When we go, we can leave behind for you all the information and scientific discoveries of those years, to enrich your world in the future. But as well as science, we can leave you other things, things to delight the ear, and the heart. Listen, now, to the music from our mother Earth.'

The lights had been turned down; the music had begun. No one who was there that night ever forgot that moment, when the first strange and beautiful sounds filled the hall. Lora stood, lost in wonder, not even remembering that Leon stood by her side, holding her hand in his.

It was a music that she had never known – the sound of things that belonged to Earth, and to Earth alone. The slow beat of deep bells, the songs of patient boatmen rowing home, of armies marching into battles long ago, the whisper of ten million voices rising from the great cities, the sound of winds dancing over endless seas of ice. All these things she heard in the music, and more – the

85

songs of distant Earth, carried to her across the light-years . . .

Then a clear high voice, rising like a bird into the sky, singing a song that went straight to every heart. It was a song for all loves lost in the loneliness of space, for friends and homes that would never be seen again, that would be forgotten for ever in years to come.

As the music died away into the darkness, the people of Thalassa, avoiding words, had gone slowly to their homes. But Lora had not gone to hers; for the loneliness that filled her heart, there was only one answer. And presently she had found it, in the warm night of the forest, as Leon's arms closed around her in the moonlight. And while the fire of love burned, they were safe from the shadows of the night and the loneliness of the stars.

To Leon, it was never wholly real. Sometimes he thought that at his journey's end Thalassa would seem like a dream that had come in his long sleep. This wild and desperate love, for example; he had not asked for it, but there it was.

When he could escape from work, he took long walks with Lora in the fields far from the village, where only machines worked on the land. For hours Lora would question him about Earth, wanting to know everything about the 'home' she had never seen with her own eyes.

She was very disappointed to hear that there were no longer great cities like Chandrigar or Astrograd on Earth, and that life there had changed so much since the old stories that she knew.

'But what happened to the cities?' she asked Leon.

'They disappeared for a number of reasons really,' Leon explained. 'When it became easy to see and talk to other people anywhere on Earth just by pushing a button on a computer, most of the need for cities was gone. Then we learnt how to turn off the pull of gravity, and once you can control gravity, you can move anything heavy, even houses, through the sky without difficulty. So all movement and travel became really simple. After that, people started to live where they liked, and the cities just slowly disappeared.'

Lora was lying on the grass, looking up at the sky. 'Do you suppose,' she said, 'that we'll ever break through the speed of light?'

'I don't think so,' he said smiling, knowing what she was thinking. 'We have to travel the slow way because that's how the universe is made, and there's nothing we can do about it.'

'It would be wonderful,' Lora said dreamily, 'to be able to travel back to Earth, to see what it was like, without spending hundreds of years on the journey.' But the wish would never come true, and with Leon beside her, it did not seem important. He was here; Earth and the stars were far away. And so also was tomorrow, with whatever unhappiness it would bring . . .

By the end of the week the engineers had built a strong metal pyramid on land that looked out over the sea. Lora, with the 571 other Palm Bay villagers and several thousand other Thalassans, came to watch the first test. Many of the islanders were nervous about the strange science of the visitors. Did the Earthmen know what they were doing? What if something went wrong? And *what* were they doing, anyway?

Lora knew that Leon was there inside the machine with his companions, preparing for the test. Then the engineers came out and walked to a high place where they stood, staring out to sea.

Two kilometres out, something strange was happening to the water. It looked like a storm, but a storm just in one small place. The waves grew higher and higher, then as tall as mountains, crashing wildly into each other. Suddenly, the movement changed. The waves came together, higher and thinner, and soon – to the amazement and fear of the watching Thalassans – a long river of sea water was rising *up* into the sky, climbing a hundred metres, then two, higher and higher, until it disappeared into the clouds above. Huge drops of water, escaping from the edge of the rising river, fell back down into the sea in a heavy rainstorm, but the river itself went on climbing up into space towards the starship *Magellan*.

Slowly the crowd moved away, forgetting their first amazement and fright. Humans had been able to control gravity for many years; now they had seen it with their own eyes. A million tonnes of water from Thalassa's sea was on its way out into space, where the engineers would freeze it and shape it, and turn it into a travelling shield for the starship. In a few days the ship would be ready to leave.

Up until the last minute, Lora had hoped that they would fail. With fear in her heart, she watched the river of water rising smoothly into the sky. It meant only one thing to her; soon she must say goodbye to Leon. She walked slowly towards the group of Earthmen, trying to stay calm. Leon saw her and came to meet her, the happiness on his face turning to worry as he saw her expression.

'Well,' he said, 'we've done it.' He sounded almost ashamed, and avoided meeting her eyes.

'And now – how long will you be here?'

'Oh, about three days – perhaps four.'

Lora had expected this. She tried to speak calmly, but the words came out as a desperate cry.

'You can't leave! Stay here on Thalassa!'

Leon took her hands and said gently, 'No, Lora – this isn't my world. I've spent half my life training for the work I'm doing now. There is no work for me here, and I would be bored to death in a month.'

'Then take me with you! I would go anywhere, do anything, if we could be together!'

'You don't really mean that. You know that you would be more out of place in my world than I would be in yours.'

But as he looked into her eyes he saw that she did mean it, and for the first time he felt ashamed of himself. He had never meant to hurt her; he was very fond of her and would always remember her. Now he was discovering, as so many men before him had done, that it was not always easy to say goodbye. There was only one thing to do. Better a short, sharp pain than a long unhappiness.

'Come with me, Lora,' he said. 'I have something to show you.' They did not speak as Leon led the way to the *Magellan*'s space bus, that great silver egg that had first brought the visitors down to Thalassa. After a short argument with another engineer there, Leon took Lora inside the bus and seconds later it had taken off, lifting smoothly into the air with no feeling of movement, no whisper of sound. Already Lora was in a world she had never known before – a world of scientific wonders that Thalassa had never needed or wanted for its life and happiness.

As Lora watched, Thalassa became just a misty curve of blue below, and soon, out of the blackness of space, the starship *Magellan* came into view. The sight of it took Lora's breath away – an endless curving wall of metal, perhaps as much as four kilometres long.

The bus found its own way home and locked itself into an entrance gate in the side of the ship. Lora followed Leon through the doors of the airlock, then stepped on to a long, moving walkway which carried them smoothly and silently into the heart of the ship.

For an hour Leon showed Lora the *Magellan*. They travelled along endless fast-moving walkways, upwards through tunnels where there was no gravity, in and out of every part of the great ship – through the engine room a kilometre long, past long rows of mysterious computers and strange machines, through huge libraries filled with every piece of information that anyone could want. The *Magellan* was a man-made and self-contained world, waiting to bring human life to a young planet far away in space. And Lora knew that Leon was showing her just how different his life was from hers.

Now they came to a great white door which slid silently open as they came near it. Inside were rows of long warm coats. Leon helped Lora to climb into one of these, and put one on himself. Then he opened a glass door in the floor, turned to her and said, 'There's no gravity down here, so keep close to me and do exactly as I say.'

Through the open door a cloud of freezing cold air was rising. Lora trembled in fear and wonder, and Leon took her arm. 'Don't worry,' he said. 'You won't notice the cold.' Then he went down through the door and Lora followed him.

Without the pull of gravity, Lora felt she was swimming, but through air rather than water. All around her, in this frozen white universe, were rows and rows of shining glass boxes, each box large enough to hold a human being.

And each box did. There they were, the thousands, tens of thousands of colonists on their way to a new world, sleeping in suspended animation until the day of their arrival. What were they dreaming in their three-hundred-year sleep? Did they dream at all in that half-world between life and death?

Overhead there were moving belts with handholds every few metres. Leon took hold of one of these and it pulled him and Lora along past the endless rows of glass boxes. They went on and on, changing from one moving belt to another, until at last Leon let go and they came to a stop beside one box no different from all the thousands of others.

But as Lora saw Leon's expression, she knew why he had brought her here, and knew that her battle was already lost.

For a long time, unconscious of the cold, Lora stared down at the sleeping woman in her glass box, a woman who would only wake long after Lora was dead. It was not a beautiful face, but it was strong, intelligent, full of character – the face of somebody able to build a new Earth beyond the stars.

At last Lora spoke, her voice a whisper in the frozen stillness.

'Is she your wife?'

'Yes. I'm sorry, Lora. I never meant to hurt you. . .'

'It doesn't matter now. It was my fault, too.' She paused and looked more closely at the sleeping woman. 'And your child as well?'

'Yes. It will be born three months after we land.'

How strange, Lora thought, to carry a child inside you for nine months and three hundred years! But that was just another part of this strange world, Leon's world, a world that had no place for her. She knew that now, and knew that the coldness that had entered her heart would stay with her long after she had left this frozen place.

She remembered nothing of the journey back to the space bus. Leon did something to the controls, and turned to her.

'Goodbye, Lora,' he said. 'My work is done. It would

be better if I stayed here on the starship.' There were no more words to say, and Lora could not even see his face through her tears.

He took her hands in his and held them hard. 'Oh Lora,' he whispered. Then he was gone.

After what seemed like a lifetime later, Lora heard an automatic voice coming from the control board. 'We have landed; please leave by the front doors.' The doors opened and Lora went through them and down the steps outside.

Surprisingly, a small crowd was watching her arrival with interest. For a moment she did not understand why; then Clyde's voice shouted, 'Where is he?' He jumped forward, his face red with anger, and caught Lora by the arm. 'Tell him to come out and meet me like a man.'

Lora shook her head tiredly. 'He's not here. I've said goodbye to him. I'll never see him again.'

Clyde stared at her disbelievingly, then saw that she spoke the truth. In the same moment Lora threw herself into his arms, crying her heart out in her pain and misery. Clyde held her close; she belonged to him again, and all his anger disappeared like morning mist in the sunshine.

For almost fifty hours the river of water thundered upwards out of the sea into space. All the island watched, through television cameras, the making of the great ice shield that would ride ahead of the *Magellan* on its way to the stars.

The last day came and went. The Earthmen said their final goodbyes, and the silver space bus lifted off and climbed up into space. Some time later the night sky exploded into light, as the starship's great engines began to burn with the fire of a thousand suns.

Lora turned her face away from the sky and hid it against Clyde's shoulder. This was where she belonged. Clyde held her gently, loving her without words, but he knew that all the days of his life, the ghost of Leon would come between him and Lora – the ghost of a man who would be not one day older when they lay dead and buried.

Already the *Magellan* was moving across the sky along its lonely and unreturning road. The white fire of its engines seemed to burn less brightly, and now the soft golden light of the moon Selene could be seen again in the sky. A few moments later the *Magellan* was only a distant point of light, then even that disappeared into the long emptiness of space.

Lora now looked up at the empty sky. Leon had been right. The life of the starship was not for her. Her life was here, on this quiet island. The colonists of the *Magellan* belonged to the future. Leon and his companions would be moving seas, levelling mountains, and fighting unknown dangers, when her descendants in two hundred years' time would still be dreaming on the peaceful beaches of Thalassa.

And which life was better, who could say?

WORD FOCUS

Use the clues below and complete this crossword with words from the story.

ACROSS

3 Leon's wife and the other people on the starship were in a deep sleep called _____ _____. They were alive, but not conscious.

5 At the beginning of the story, Lora could see Clyde's boat on the _____, the line at which the land and the sea seem to meet.

6 At the dance, Clyde drank too much alcohol and got very _____.

7 Lora's father was the _____ of Palm Bay, the chief official.

8 Earth is one of the nine _____ which move around our sun.

DOWN

1 Humans had learned how to turn off _____, the force that on Earth pulls things towards the centre of the planet.

2 The starship was carrying _____ to a new home on a new planet.

3 The new _____ to protect the starship in space was made of ice.

4 To move the water into space, the engineers built a metal _____, square at the bottom with four sides that went up and met at the top.

STORY FOCUS 1

What is 'love at first sight'? Do you think it can really happen? Why or why not? Discuss your ideas with a partner and give reasons for your opinions. Then read this short passage from page 76, and answer the questions below.

> Words of welcome were spoken, hands were shaken, but Lora saw and heard none of it, because in that moment, she saw Leon for the first time.

1 What do you think is happening to Lora at this moment?
2 Look for three more sentences which describe Lora's or Leon's experience of love at first sight. Write your answers in the boxes.

1
2
3

STORY FOCUS 2

Here are six different titles for the story. Which do you think is best? Why? Can you suggest some more titles of your own?

1 **A Strange New Land**   2 **Love at First Sight**

3 **Lost Love?**

4 *A Second Chance*   5 Forbidden Fruit

6 **Helpless**

Feuille d'Album

~

We have all tried to help him, but there's something a little strange about Ian. Most young artists living on their own in Paris would be happy to have a group of older women looking after them, taking an interest, being kind . . . But not Ian. We've tried to mother him, to fall in love with him, even to take him out drinking in night-clubs.

Yes, there's something rather odd about Ian French, but we just don't know what it is . . .

Feuille d'Album

Retold by Rosalie Kerr

He really was an impossible person. Too shy, and he had nothing at all to say. When he came to your studio, he just sat there, silent. When he finally went, blushing red all over his face, you wanted to scream and throw something at him.

The strange thing was that at first sight he looked most interesting. Everybody agreed about that. You saw him in a café one evening, sitting in a corner with a glass of coffee in front of him. He was a thin, dark boy, who always wore a blue shirt and a grey jacket that was a little too small for him. He looked just like a boy who has decided to run away to sea. You expected him to get up at any moment, and walk out into the night and be drowned.

He had short black hair, grey eyes, white skin and a mouth that always looked ready for tears. Oh, just to see him did something to your heart! And he had this habit of blushing. If a waiter spoke to him, he turned red!

'Who is he, my dear? Do you know?'

'Yes. His name is Ian French. He paints. They say he's very clever. Someone I know tried to mother him. She asked him how often he had a letter from home, if he had enough blankets on his bed, how much milk he drank. Then she went to his studio to make sure he had enough clean shirts. She rang and rang the bell, but nobody came to the door, although she was sure he was there . . . Hopeless!'

Someone else decided he ought to fall in love. She called him to her, took his hand, and told him how wonderful life can be for those who are brave. But when she went to his studio one evening, she rang and rang . . . Hopeless.

'What the poor boy really needs is excitement,' a third woman said. She took him to cafés and night-clubs, dark places where the drinks cost too much and there were always stories of a shooting the night before. Once he got very drunk, but still he said nothing, and when she took him home to his studio, he just said 'goodnight' and left her outside in the street . . . Hopeless.

Other women tried to help him – women can be *very* kind – but finally they, too, were defeated. We are all busy people, and why should we spend our valuable time on someone who refuses to be helped?

'And anyway, I think there is something rather odd about him, don't you agree? He can't be as innocent as he looks. Why come to Paris if you don't intend to have any fun?'

He lived at the top of a tall, ugly building, near the river. As it was so high, the studio had a wonderful view. From the two big windows he could see boats on the river and an island covered with trees. From the side window he looked across to a smaller and uglier house, and down below there was a flower market. You could see the tops of huge umbrellas with bright flowers around them, and plants in boxes. Old women moved backwards and forwards among the flowers. Really, he didn't need to go out. There was always something to draw.

If any kind woman had been able to get into his studio, she would have had a surprise. He kept it as neat as a pin. Everything was arranged in its place, exactly like a painting – the bowl of eggs, the cups and the teapot on the shelf, the books and the lamp on the table. There was a red Indian cover on his bed, and on the wall by the bed there was a small, neatly written notice: GET UP AT ONCE.

Every day was the same. When the light was good he painted, then cooked a meal and tidied the studio. In the evenings he went to the café or sat at home reading or writing a list which began: 'What I can afford to spend'. The list ended 'I promise not to spend more this month. Signed, Ian French.'

Nothing odd about that; but the women were right. There was something else.

One evening he was sitting at the side window eating an apple and looking down on to the tops of the huge umbrellas in the empty flower market. It had been raining, the first spring rain of the year, and the air smelled of plants and wet earth. Down below in the market, the trees were covered in new green. 'What kind of trees are they?' he wondered. He stared down at the small ugly house, and suddenly two windows opened like wings and a girl came out on to the balcony, carrying a pot of daffodils. She was a strangely thin girl in a dark dress, with a pink handkerchief tied over her hair.

'Yes, it is warm enough. It will do them good,' she said, putting down the pot, and turning to someone in the room inside. As she turned, she put her hands up to her hair to tidy it, and looked down at the market and up at the sky. She did not look at the house opposite. Then she disappeared.

His heart fell out of the window and down to the balcony, where it buried itself among the green leaves of the daffodils.

The room with the balcony was the sitting-room, and next to it was the kitchen. He heard her washing the dishes after supper, saw her come to the window to shake out the tablecloth. She never sang or combed her hair or stared at the moon as young girls are said to do. She always wore the same dark dress and pink handkerchief.

Who did she live with? Nobody else came to the window, but she was always talking to someone. Her mother, he decided, was always ill. They took in sewing work. The father was dead . . . He had been a journalist. By working all day she and her mother just made enough money to live on, but they never went out and they had no friends.

He had to make some new notices . . . 'Not to go to the window before six o'clock: signed, Ian French. Not to think about her until he had finished his painting for the day: signed, Ian French.'

It was quite simple. She was the only person he wanted to know because she was, he decided, the only person alive who was exactly his age. He didn't want silly girls, and he had no use for older women. She was his age. She was – well, just like him.

He sat in his studio, staring at her windows, seeing himself in those rooms with her. She was often angry. They had terrible fights, he and she. And she rarely laughed. Only sometimes, when she told him about a funny little cat she once had, who used to scratch and pretend to be fierce when she gave it meat to eat . . . Things like that made her laugh. Usually, they sat together very quietly, talking in low voices, or silent and tired after the day's work. Of course, she never asked him about his pictures, and of course he painted the most wonderful pictures of her, which she hated because he made her so thin and so dark . . .

But how could he meet her?

Then he discovered that once a week, in the evening, she went shopping. On two Thursdays he saw her at the window in a coat, carrying a basket. The next Thursday, at the same time, he ran down the stairs. There was a lovely pink light over everything. He saw it reflected in the river, and the people walking towards him in the street had pink faces and pink hands.

Outside the house he waited for her. He had no idea what he was going to do or say. 'Here she comes,' said a voice in his head. She walked very quickly, with small, light steps . . . What could he do? He could only follow . . .

First she went to buy some bread. Then she went to a fish shop. She had to wait a long time in there. Then she went to the fruit shop and bought an orange. As he watched her, he knew more surely than ever that he must talk to her, now. Her seriousness and her loneliness, even the way she walked – separate, somehow, distant from the other people in the street – all this was so natural, so right to him.

'Yes, she is always like that,' he thought proudly. 'She and I are different from these people.'

But now she was going home, and he had not spoken to her. Then she went into another shop. Through the window, he saw her buying an egg. She took it carefully out of the basket – a brown egg, a beautiful one, the one he himself would have chosen. She came out of the shop, and he went in. A moment later he was out again, following her through the flower market, past the huge umbrellas, walking on fallen flowers.

He followed her into the house and up the stairs. She stopped at a door and took a key out of her purse. As she put the key in the lock, he ran up to her.

Blushing redder than ever, but looking straight at her, he said, almost angrily: 'Excuse me, Mademoiselle, you dropped this.'

And he gave her an egg.

WORD FOCUS

These word jumbles have the letters in the wrong order. Put the letters in the correct order to make a word which will fit the gap in each sentence. Here is an example:

atdpine   Every day, when the light was good, Ian *painted*.

1 **ulgshnbi**   Ian was very shy and had the habit of _____ when he was embarrassed.
2 **nrudk**   One night in a bar Ian got very _____, but he still said nothing to the woman who had invited him.
3 **istduo**   Ian was an artist, and both lived and worked in his _____.
4 **dsffdaoil**   Ian first saw the girl carrying a pot of _____.
5 **yblaocn**   The girl opened the windows and stepped out onto the _____.
6 **aencdhkrefhi**   When Ian first saw the girl, she had a pink _____ tied over her hair.

Later, perhaps, the girl wrote some notes in her diary. Use five of the six words above to fill in the gaps.

Today something very strange happened. There's a young artist who lives and works in a _____ near my house. A few weeks ago, when I went out onto the _____ one night to put the _____ outside for the spring, I felt someone watching me. It must have been this same young man because tonight he ran up to me at our door. His face was very red, and he seemed angry. At first I was a little afraid because I thought he was _____, but then I realized that he was _____ because he was embarrassed. The really strange thing was this – he gave me an egg, saying I had dropped it. But if I had really dropped my egg, it would have smashed!

STORY FOCUS 1

Here are notes for two different endings for the story. Choose the idea you prefer, and then use the notes to write a paragraph for your new ending.

1 / The girl happy / her apartment / her grandmother / painting her picture in his studio / café at night / quiet wedding / quiet, simple life /

2 / The girl shocked / boyfriend / grandmother angry /fighting in the house / police / lonely / studio /

STORY FOCUS 2

The author uses the point of view of several women to introduce us to Ian French. Here are some of the things that the women say about Ian. For each phrase, explain your understanding of what the women are telling us about him.

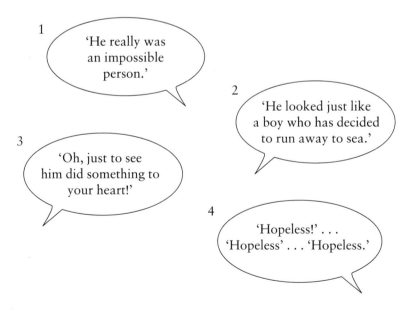

1 'He really was an impossible person.'

2 'He looked just like a boy who has decided to run away to sea.'

3 'Oh, just to see him did something to your heart!'

4 'Hopeless!' . . . 'Hopeless' . . . 'Hopeless.'

The Doll's House

~

Everybody at school wanted to see the doll's house that the three Burnell children had been given. It was so perfect, so wonderful. Isabel, Lottie, and Kezia couldn't wait to show it to their friends. Their mother said they could ask the girls at school, two at a time, to come and see it.

Of course, mother didn't mean that all the girls at school were invited to the house. The Kelveys weren't invited – they never were. Nobody spoke to the Kelveys . . . They were *different* . . .

KATHERINE MANSFIELD

The Doll's House

Retold by Rosalie Kerr

When dear old Mrs Hay went home after staying with the Burnells, she sent the children a doll's house. It was so big that Pat, the hired man, could only just lift it, and they had to leave it outside in the garden. It was all right there; it was summer. And perhaps the smell of paint would go before they had to take it indoors. Really, the smell of paint (so sweet of dear, generous Mrs Hay!) – but the smell of paint was so strong that it was enough to make anyone seriously ill, or so Aunt Beryl thought. You could smell the paint even when it was wrapped up. And when they unwrapped it . . .

There it stood, a doll's house, painted a thick, dark, oily green. Its two solid little chimneys were painted red and white, and it had a bright yellow door and real glass windows.

It was perfect! Who cared about the smell? It was part of the wonder of the doll's house, part of the newness.

'Open it quickly, someone!'

The fastening at the side was stuck fast, and Pat had to use his knife to get it open. But then . . . the whole front of the house swung back and – you could see everything! The sitting-room, the kitchen, the two bedrooms. That is the way for a house to open! Why don't all houses do that?

How exciting, to be able to see everything you want to see, all at once!

'Oh – oh!' The Burnell children were quite unable to speak. It was too wonderful. They had never seen anything like it in their lives. There was paper on the walls, and pictures, just like in real houses. There was red carpet on the floors, except in the kitchen; red and green chairs, beds with real covers on them, tiny plates and cups.

But what Kezia liked more than anything, what she liked most awfully, was the lamp. It stood in the middle of the table, a beautiful little gold and white lamp, all ready to be lit. Of course, you couldn't really light it, but there was something inside it that looked like oil and moved when you shook it.

The mother and father dolls sitting stiffly in their chairs and their two little children in bed upstairs were really too big for the doll's house. They didn't look quite right. But the lamp was perfect. It seemed to smile at Kezia, to say, 'I live here.' The lamp was real.

The Burnell children could not walk to school fast enough the next morning. They burned to tell everybody about the doll's house.

'I shall describe it,' said Isabel, 'because I'm the eldest. You two can join in, but I must speak first.'

Lottie and Kezia said nothing. Isabel was bossy, but she was always right.

'And I shall choose who's going to come and see it first,' Isabel said. 'Mother said I could.'

Their mother had told them that they could ask the girls at school, two at a time, to come and see the doll's house. Of course, they were not invited to tea, or to come into the house, but they could come into the garden and stand there quietly, while Isabel showed them all the lovely things in the doll's house.

It was too bad that they arrived at school just as the bell was ringing, and they had no time to talk to anyone. Never mind! Isabel looked very important and mysterious, and whispered to some of her friends, 'I've got something to tell you at play-time!'

When play-time came, everyone wanted to be near Isabel. The little girls almost fought to put their arms around her, to walk beside her and be her special friend. Laughing and pushing one another, they gathered closely around her. The only two who stayed outside the circle were the two who were always outside – the Kelveys. They knew they were not wanted.

To be perfectly honest, the school the Burnell children went to was not the kind of school their parents really wanted for them. But they had no choice. It was the only school for miles. And because of this, all the children in the area, the Judge's little girls, the doctor's daughters and all the children of milkmen and farmers, were forced to mix together. And there were plenty of rude, rough little boys, too. But worst of all, there were the Kelveys. The Burnell children were not allowed to speak to them. They walked past the Kelveys with their heads in the air. And because others followed where the Burnells led, nobody spoke to the Kelveys. Even the teacher had a special voice for them, and a special smile for the other children when Lil Kelvey came up to her desk to give her some very tired-looking flowers she had picked by the side of the road.

They were the daughters of a neat, hard-working little woman, who went from house to house, doing people's washing for them. This was awful enough. But where was Mr Kelvey? Nobody knew. But everybody said he was in prison. So they were the daughters of a woman who washed people's clothes and a man who was in prison. Very nice companions for other people's children!

Then there was the way they looked. It was hard to understand why Mrs Kelvey dressed them in such an odd way. The truth was, she made their clothes from old bits and pieces which were given to her by the people she worked for. Lil, for example, who was a solid, plain child, came to school in a dress made out of an old green tablecloth of the Burnells, and a red curtain that had belonged to the Logans. Her hat came from Miss Lecky at the post office, and had a long red feather stuck in it. What a sight she looked! It was impossible not to laugh.

And her little sister, 'our Else', as Lil always called her, wore a long white dress that looked like a night-dress, and a pair of boy's boots. But our Else would have looked strange in any clothes. She was a tiny white creature with huge eyes – just like a little bird. Nobody had ever seen her smile; she hardly ever spoke. Everywhere Lil went, our Else followed, holding a piece of Lil's skirt in her hand. In the playground or on the road to or from school, you could always see Lil, with our Else close behind her. When she wanted something, our Else pulled on Lil's skirt, and Lil stopped and turned around. The Kelveys always understood one another.

Now they stood at the edge of the circle, outside the group of friends. You couldn't stop them listening. When the little girls turned round and gave them angry looks, Lil, as usual, smiled all over her silly red face, but our Else just stared and said nothing.

Isabel talked on, in a proud voice. She described the carpet, the beds with real covers, the kitchen with its tiny cups and plates.

When she finished, Kezia said, 'You've forgotten the lamp, Isabel.'

'Oh yes,' said Isabel. 'There's a lovely little lamp on the table. It's just like a real one.'

'The lamp's best of all,' cried Kezia. She wanted Isabel to talk for longer about the lamp, to let everyone know how special it was. But nobody was listening to Kezia. Isabel was choosing the first two who were going to come and see the doll's house. She chose Emmie Cole and Lena Logan. But all the others knew that they would have a chance to see it another day. They all wanted to be nice to Isabel. They all had a secret to whisper to her. 'Isabel's *my* friend.'

Only the little Kelveys were forgotten. There was nothing more for them to hear.

Days passed, and more and more children were taken to see the doll's house. It was the one thing they talked about. 'Have you seen the Burnells' doll's house? Oh, isn't it lovely? Haven't you seen it yet? Oh, dear!'

The little girls talked about the doll's house at dinner-time, as they sat under the trees in the school playground, eating their thick meat sandwiches and buttered cake. The little Kelveys listened, while they ate their bread and butter out of a piece of newspaper.

'Mother,' said Kezia, 'please can I ask the Kelveys, just once?'

'Of course not, Kezia.'

'But why not?'

'Run away, Kezia. You know why not.'

At last the day came when everyone except the Kelveys had seen the doll's house. That day, there was less to talk about. It was dinner-time. The little girls sat together under the trees, and suddenly, as they looked at the Kelveys eating out of their piece of newspaper, they wanted to be unkind to them.

Emmie Cole started it. 'Lil Kelvey's going to be a servant when she grows up,' she whispered.

'Oh, how awful!' said Isabel Burnell.

Emmie looked at Isabel in a way she had seen her mother look, when she was talking about things like this.

'It's true,' she said.

Then Lena Logan joined in. 'Shall I ask her?' she said.

'You don't dare,' said Jessie May.

'Oh, I'm not frightened,' said Lena. She laughed and did a little dance in front of the other girls. 'Watch! Watch me now!' she said, and she danced right over to the Kelveys.

Lil looked up from her bread and butter. Our Else stopped eating. What was coming now?

'Is it true that you're going to be a servant when you grow up, Lil Kelvey?' Lena screamed at her.

Silence. Lil gave no answer, but she smiled her silly, red-faced smile. She didn't seem to mind the question at all. Poor Lena! The other girls began to laugh at her.

Lena didn't like that. She stepped right up to Lil. 'Yah, your father's in prison!' she shouted in her face.

This was so wonderful to hear that all the little girls rushed away together, deeply excited by what Lena had done. How fast they ran, how high they jumped, how wild and free they felt that morning!

In the afternoon, Pat came to take the Burnell children home. There were visitors. Isabel and Lottie, who liked visitors, went upstairs to change their dresses, but Kezia slipped quietly out into the garden. There was nobody there. She began to swing on the big white garden gate. Then, looking down the road, she saw two little figures coming towards her, one in front, the other close behind. It was the Kelveys. She got down from the gate. For a moment she thought about running away. The Kelveys came nearer. Then Kezia climbed back up on the gate. She had decided what she must do. She started swinging on the gate again.

'Hello,' she said to the Kelveys.

They were so surprised that they stopped. Lil gave her silly smile. Our Else stared.

'You can come and see our doll's house if you want to,' Kezia said.

Lil turned red. She shook her head.

'Why not?' asked Kezia.

'Your ma told our ma you mustn't speak to us.'

'Oh, well,' said Kezia. She didn't know what to say. 'It doesn't matter. But you can still come and see our doll's house. Come on. Nobody's looking.'

But Lil shook her head again.

'Don't you want to?' asked Kezia.

Suddenly, there was a pull on Lil's skirt. She turned round. Our Else was looking at her with big, desperate eyes. She wanted to see the doll's house. Lil looked at her very doubtfully. But then our Else pulled her skirt again. Lil stepped forwards. Like two little lost cats, they followed Kezia across the garden to where the doll's house stood.

'There it is,' said Kezia.

They said nothing. Lil breathed loudly. Our Else was as still as stone.

'I'll open it for you,' said Kezia kindly. 'Look, here's the sitting-room and the kitchen, and that's the—'

'Kezia!'

Oh, how they jumped!

'Kezia!'

It was Aunt Beryl's voice. They turned round. She was standing at the back door, staring at them. Aunt Beryl just couldn't believe her eyes.

'How dare you bring the little Kelveys into our garden!' she said to Kezia, in a cold, angry voice. 'You know as well as I do that you aren't allowed to talk to them.'

'Run away, children, run away and don't come back!' she said to the Kelveys. 'Off you go immediately!'

She did not have to tell them twice. They were out of the garden in a moment, Lil red-faced and ashamed, with our Else hanging onto her skirt.

'Bad, disobedient little girl!' Aunt Beryl said bitterly to Kezia, and she closed the doll's house with a bang.

Aunt Beryl had been having a terrible day, but now that she had got rid of those little animals the Kelveys and shouted at Kezia, she felt a lot better. She went back into the house singing.

When the Kelveys were far away from the Burnells' house, they stopped and sat down by the side of the road. Lil's face was still burning, and she took off her hat. They stared across the fields, where the Logans' cows were eating grass. What were the little Kelveys thinking?

Our Else moved closer to her sister. She had already forgotten the angry lady. She put out a finger and touched the feather on Lil's hat. She smiled her rare smile.

'I seen the little lamp,' she said softly.

Then both were silent once more.

WORD FOCUS

Use the clues below and complete this crossword with words from the story.

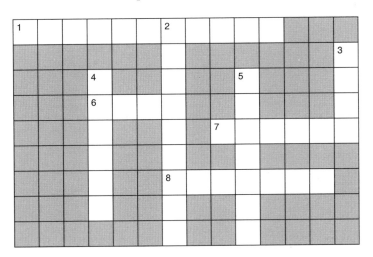

ACROSS

1 When Kezia invited the Kelveys into the garden, Aunt Beryl was very angry with her and called her 'a _____ little girl'.

6 Our Else was very happy because she saw the little _____.

7 Even though nobody knew the Kelvey girls' father, everyone said that he was in _____.

8 When Aunt Beryl spoke angrily to the children, Lil felt _____.

DOWN

2 When Else really wanted to see the doll's house, she looked up at her sister with big, _____ eyes.

3 At the end of the story, Else said, 'I _____ the little lamp.' This is a non-standard form of 'I saw' often used by uneducated speakers.

4 In the Burnell family there were three girls, and Isabel was the _____.

5 The girls at school said that Lil Kelvey was going to be a _____ when she grew up.

117

STORY FOCUS 1

Later the same day perhaps Lil talked to her mother. Complete their conversation. Use as many words as you like.

MOTHER: What's the matter, Lil? Have you been crying?

LIL: It's the girls at school. They say things like _____.

MOTHER: You mustn't let it worry you, Lil. They're just children.

LIL: But why _____?

MOTHER: I don't know. Perhaps because they hear their parents saying them.

LIL: Today Else wanted to see _____.

MOTHER: And what happened? Did you see it?

LIL: Yes, but a woman in the Burnells' house _____.

MOTHER: Well, you shouldn't have been in their garden, should you?

LIL: But Kezia Burnell _____.

MOTHER: Oh. That was nice of her. Did she get into trouble too?

LIL: Yes, the woman _____.

STORY FOCUS 2

The Kelvey girls are described as 'the two who were always outside'. Find three sentences or short passages in the story which show that the Kelveys were outsiders, and write them down.

Do you think Kezia is different from her sisters and her friends? In what way? Discuss your answer with a partner.

1 _____

_____

2 _____

_____

3 _____

_____

About the
Authors

~

ARTHUR C. CLARKE

Arthur Charles Clarke (1917–2008) was born in Somerset, England. From an early age he was interested in everything scientific, building his own wireless sets, telescopes to look at the moon, and several home-made rockets. He was also an enthusiastic reader and collector of science-fiction magazines. In 1946 he published his first science-fiction short story, and two years later gained a degree in physics and mathematics from London University. He travelled widely, published several successful novels, and became a keen deep-sea diver. From 1956 until his death in 2008, he lived in Sri Lanka, in a house full of computers and all kinds of modern electronic technology.

Arthur C. Clarke lectured in Britain and the United States, made many radio and television appearances, and wrote about eighty books and five hundred articles and short stories. He received many awards, and was famous both for his science writing – on space flight, scientific forecasting, and undersea exploration – and for his inventive and technologically detailed science fiction. His greatest success was probably *2001: A Space Odyssey* (1968) – he wrote the novel and co-authored the screenplay for the famous Stanley Kubrick film.

All his life he had a deep interest in the meeting point between science and science fiction. Many of his predictions have come true, and what is fiction today might easily become the fact of tomorrow. In a book he published in 1962, he wrote, 'Any sufficiently advanced technology is indistinguishable from magic.'

ROBYN DAVIDSON

Robyn Davidson (1950–) was born on a cattle station in Queensland, Australia, but after the death of her mother she was brought up by her aunt in the city. After some restless years, she set out for Alice Springs, in the centre of Australia. At that time, she wrote, she had 'never changed a light bulb, sewn a dress, mended a sock, changed a tyre, or used a screwdriver'. She spent some time learning to train camels, and in 1977 she set out from Alice Springs with four camels and a dog to walk to the west coast, a journey of about 2,800 kilometres across the great Australian desert. It was a journey of discovery about herself, but two years later she wrote a book about it, called *Tracks*, which made her famous. It won the 1980 Thomas Cook Travel Book Award, became an international bestseller, and has been translated into sixteen languages.

Her Australian journey began a lifetime of travel and adventure, and she has spent the past thirty years travelling and writing about her travels. She has published a novel, *Ancestors*, and a collection of essays, *Travelling Light*. In the early 1990s, she spent nearly two years with the nomadic Rabari people of Rajasthan, in northwest India, as they made their yearly journey across the desert with their camels and goats. The Rabari women were very kind to her, but 'it was an extremely, extremely difficult journey,' she said in an interview. 'It wasn't a light experience. It was hell.' Her book about her experiences with the Rabari people, *Desert Places*, came out in 1996.

Robyn Davidson has lived at more than forty addresses over the years, and has had homes in Sydney, London, and the Indian Himalayas. She said in an interview in 2008 on Australian television that she had 'chosen freedom over comfort, which means that I've often been uncomfortable'. But she is still restless, still full of travelling plans for the future.

M. R. JAMES

Montague Rhodes James (1862–1936) was born in Kent, England. He was a clever student, and was very interested in the ancient world; he won prizes for writing in Latin, and studied archaeology, history, and Christian art and architecture. He spent his life teaching and writing in two great colleges – King's College, Cambridge, and Eton College, a famous boys' school.

James published many books and papers on his studies, but he is best remembered today for his ghost stories. He only wrote about thirty of them, but many people think he is one of the best writers of ghost stories there has ever been. He had three rules for writing ghost stories: there should be no long and complicated information about ghostly practices; the stories should happen in ordinary places and to ordinary people; and, most importantly, the ghost should be evil and eager to hurt or frighten people. Because of his studies, James knew a lot about ancient places, old churches and buildings, and in these calm and peaceful settings he quietly leads his readers to the horror waiting in the shadows. All these things together make his stories very powerful, and many other writers have studied his stories carefully, and tried to make theirs as good.

James, known as 'Monty' to his friends, was not just a dry scholar. He was very popular with students, enjoyed the theatre, and used to read his own ghost stories out loud to his friends, while sitting by the fireside at Christmas. He was often asked if he believed in ghosts himself, but he was too clever a scholar to give a clear answer one way or the other. In the introduction to one of his books he wrote: 'Do I believe in ghosts? I am prepared to consider evidence and accept it if it satisfies me.'

KATHERINE MANSFIELD

Katherine Mansfield (1888–1923) was born Kathleen Mansfield Beauchamp in Wellington, New Zealand. Her father was a wealthy banker, and Katherine, with her brother and three sisters, had a comfortable life as a child. At the age of fourteen she was sent to London to finish her education, and she spent most of the rest of her short life in Europe.

From an early age, Katherine felt different from her family. She studied music for a time, and was already writing stories while still at school. She spent her life among writers and artists, and her friends included some famous authors of the time, such as D. H. Lawrence and Virginia Woolf.

Although she married twice, Katherine never lived an ordinary family life. From the age of twenty, she suffered from a serious disease, and in search of better health, she spent part of every year in France and Switzerland. She wrote a large number of short stories, even though it was often difficult for her to find the strength and peace she needed in order to write. She died in France, aged only thirty-five.

Her first book, *In a German Pension*, appeared in 1911, followed by *Prelude* in 1916, *Bliss* in 1921, and *The Garden Party and Other Stories* in 1922. Two more books of stories, her letters, and her journal were published after her death.

She is considered to be one of the finest writers of her time, and has often been compared to the Russian writer Chekhov. Her sensitive, delicate stories take the reader straight into the lives of her characters, who are often women struggling to survive in an unfriendly world.

READING CIRCLE ROLES

When you work on your role sheet, remember these words:

~ READ ~ THINK ~ CONNECT ~ ASK ~~ AND CONNECT

READ ~

- Read the story once without stopping.
- Read it again while you work on your role sheet.

THINK ~

- Look for passages in the story that are interesting or unusual. Think about them. Prepare some questions to ask about them.
- Think about the meanings of words. If you use a dictionary, try to use an English-to-English learner's dictionary.

CONNECT ~

- Connect with the characters' thoughts and feelings. Perhaps it is a horror story and we cannot 'connect' with an experience like this, but we can see how the characters are thinking or feeling.

ASK ~

- Ask questions with many possible answers; questions that begin with *How? Why? What? Who?* Do not ask *yes/no* questions.
- When you ask questions, use English words that everyone in your circle can understand, so that everyone can talk about the story.

AND CONNECT ~

- Connect with your circle. Share your ideas, listen to other people's ideas. If you don't understand something, ask people to repeat or explain. And have fun!

The role sheets are on the next six pages (and on page 138 there are role badges you can make). Bigger role sheets, with space for writing, are in the Teacher's Handbook. Or you can read about your role in these pages, and write your notes and questions in your own notebook.

Discussion Leader

STORY: _____

NAME: _____

The Discussion Leader's job is to . . .

- read the story twice, and prepare at least five general questions about it.
- ask one or two questions to start the Reading Circle discussion.
- make sure that everyone has a chance to speak and joins in the discussion.
- call on each member to present their prepared role information.
- guide the discussion and keep it going.

Usually the best discussion questions come from your own thoughts, feelings, and questions as you read. (What surprised you, made you smile, made you feel sad?) Write down your questions as soon as you have finished reading. It is best to use your own questions, but you can also use some of the ideas at the bottom of this page.

MY QUESTIONS:

1 _____

— _____

— _____

— _____

— _____

— _____

— _____

Other general ideas:

- Questions about the characters (*like / not like them, true to life / not true to life* ...?)
- Questions about the theme (*friendship, romance, parents/children, ghosts* ...?)
- Questions about the ending (*surprising, expected, liked it / did not like it* ...?)
- Questions about what will happen next. (These can also be used for a longer story.)

Summarizer

STORY: _____

NAME: _____

The Summarizer's job is to . . .

- read the story and make notes about the characters, events, and ideas.
- find the key points that everyone must know to understand and remember the story.
- retell the story in a short summary (one or two minutes) in your own words.
- talk about your summary to the group, using your writing to help you.

Your reading circle will find your summary very useful, because it will help to remind them of the plot and the characters in the story. You may need to read the story more than once to make a good summary, and you may need to repeat it to the group a second time.

MY KEY POINTS:

Main events:

Characters:

MY SUMMARY:

Connector

STORY: _____

NAME: _____

The Connector's job is to . . .

- read the story twice, and look for connections between the story and the world outside.
- make notes about at least two possible connections to your own experiences, or to the experiences of friends and family, or to real-life events.
- tell the group about the connections and ask for their comments or questions.
- ask the group if they can think of any connections themselves.

These questions will help you think about connections while you are reading.

Events: Has anything similar ever happened to you, or to someone you know? Does anything in the story remind you of events in the real world? For example, events you have read about in newspapers, or heard about on television news programmes.

Characters: Do any of them remind you of people you know? How? Why? Have you ever had the same thoughts or feelings as these characters have? Do you know anybody who thinks, feels, behaves like that?

MY CONNECTIONS:

1 _____

— _____

— _____

— _____

— _____

— _____

— _____

— _____

Word Master

STORY: _____

NAME: _____

The Word Master's job is to . . .

- read the story, and look for words or short phrases that are new or difficult to understand, or that are important in the story.
- choose five words (only five) that you think are important for this story.
- explain the meanings of these five words in simple English to the group.
- tell the group why these words are important for understanding this story.

Your five words do not have to be new or unknown words. Look for words in the story that really stand out in some way. These may be words that are:

- repeated often   • used in an unusual way   • important to the meaning of the story

MY WORDS	MEANING OF THE WORD	REASON FOR CHOOSING THE WORD
PAGE _____ LINE _____		
PAGE _____ LINE _____		
PAGE _____ LINE _____		
PAGE _____ LINE _____		
PAGE _____ LINE _____		

Passage Person

STORY: _____

NAME: _____

The Passage Person's job is to . . .

- read the story, and find important, interesting, or difficult passages.
- make notes about at least three passages that are important for the plot, or that explain the characters, or that have very interesting or powerful language.
- read each passage to the group, or ask another group member to read it.
- ask the group one or two questions about each passage.

A passage is usually one paragraph, but sometimes it can be just one or two sentences, or perhaps a piece of dialogue. You might choose a passage to discuss because it is:

- important   - informative   - surprising   - funny   - confusing   - well-written

MY PASSAGES:

PAGE _____ **LINES** _____

REASONS FOR CHOOSING THE PASSAGE	QUESTIONS ABOUT THE PASSAGE

PAGE _____ **LINES** _____

REASONS FOR CHOOSING THE PASSAGE	QUESTIONS ABOUT THE PASSAGE

PAGE _____ **LINES** _____

REASONS FOR CHOOSING THE PASSAGE	QUESTIONS ABOUT THE PASSAGE

Culture Collector

STORY: _____

NAME: _____

The Culture Collector's job is to . . .

- read the story, and look for both differences and similarities between your own culture and the culture found in the story.
- make notes about two or three passages that show these cultural points.
- read each passage to the group, or ask another group member to read it.
- ask the group some questions about these, and any other cultural points in the story.

Here are some questions to help you think about cultural differences.

Theme: What is the theme of this story (for example, getting married, meeting a ghost, murder, unhappy children)? Is this an important theme in your own culture? Do people think about this theme in the same way, or differently?

People: Do characters in this story say or do things that people never say or do in your culture? Do they say or do some things that everybody in the world says or does?

MY CULTURAL COLLECTION (differences and similarities):

1 **PAGE** _____ **LINES** _____ : _____

_____

2 **PAGE** _____ **LINES** _____ : _____

_____

MY CULTURAL QUESTIONS:

— _____

— _____

— _____

— _____

PLOT PYRAMID ACTIVITY

A **plot** is a series of events which form a story. The Reading Circles **Plot Pyramid** is a way of looking at and talking about the plot of a story. The pyramid divides the story into five parts.

The Exposition gives the background needed to understand the story. It tells us who the characters are, where the story happens, and when it happens. Sometimes we also get an idea about problems to come.

The Complication is the single event which begins the conflict, or creates the problem. The event might be an action, a thought, or words spoken by one of the characters.

The Rising Action brings more events and difficulties. As the story moves through these events, it gets more exciting, and begins to take us toward the climax.

The Climax is the high point of the story, the turning point, the point of no return. It marks a change, for better or for worse, in the lives of one or more of the characters.

The Resolution usually offers an answer to the problem or the conflict, which may be sad or happy for the characters. Mysteries are explained, secrets told, and the reader can feel calm again.

HOW TO PLOT THE PYRAMID

1 Read your story again, and look for each part of the pyramid as you read. Make notes, or mark your book.

2 In your Reading Circle, find each part of the pyramid in the story, and then write down your ideas. Use the boxes in the diagram opposite as a guide (a bigger diagram, with space for writing in the boxes, is in the Teacher's Handbook).

3 Begin with the *Exposition*, and work through the *Complication*, the *Rising Action* (only two points), the *Climax*, and the *Resolution*.

4 Finally, your group draws the pyramid and writes the notes on the board, and then presents the pyramid to the class.

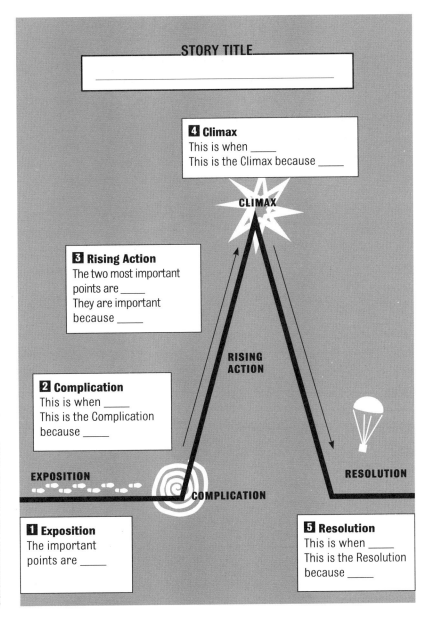

STORY TITLE

4 Climax
This is when _____
This is the Climax because _____

CLIMAX

3 Rising Action
The two most important
points are _____
They are important
because _____

RISING
ACTION

2 Complication
This is when _____
This is the Complication
because _____

EXPOSITION

COMPLICATION

RESOLUTION

1 Exposition
The important
points are _____

5 Resolution
This is when _____
This is the Resolution
because _____

POSTER ACTIVITY

Each Reading Circle group makes a poster in English about a story in this book. Posters can have words, pictures, and drawings. Your group will need to find extra information about the story – perhaps from the Internet, or the school library, or your teacher.

Use the ideas on the opposite page to help you. When all the posters are finished, each Reading Circle will present their own poster to the other groups. At the end, keep all the posters, and make a 'poster library'.

STORY TITLE

THE THEME

What is the theme of the story?

- Is it about love or murder or friendship? Is it about dreams or wishes or fears?

THE TIME, THE PLACE

What do you know about the time and the place of the story?

- the city / the country?
- a real world, or an unreal world?
- If the time and place are not given, does it matter?

THE WRITER

What interesting facts do you know about the author's life?

- Was he or she also a poet, an actor, a teacher? Or a spy, a sailor, a thief, a doctor, a madman?

THE BACKGROUND

What cultural information did you learn from the story?

- About family events (for example, a wedding)
- A national holiday
- Family life (for example, parents and children)

THE LANGUAGE

What did you like about the language in the story?

- Find a quotation you like – words that are funny or clever or sad, or words that paint a picture in your mind.

THE FILM

Direct your own film! Who will play the characters in the film?

- Choose the best actors to play the characters.
- Where will you film it?
- Will you change the story?
- What title will the film have?

BOOKWORMS CLUB
Stories for Reading Circles
Editor: Mark Furr

The Bookworms Club brings together selections of adapted short stories at different levels from other Bookworms titles. These stories have been specially chosen for use with Reading Circles.

BOOKWORMS CLUB BRONZE
STAGES 1 AND 2

The Horse of Death by Sait Faik, from *The Meaning of Gifts: Stories from Turkey*

The Little Hunters at the Lake by Yalvac Ural, from *The Meaning of Gifts: Stories from Turkey*

Mr Harris and the Night Train by Jennifer Bassett, from *One-Way Ticket*

Sister Love by John Escott, from *Sister Love and Other Crime Stories*

Omega File 349: London, England by Jennifer Bassett, from *The Omega Files*

Tildy's Moment by O. Henry, from *New Yorkers*

Andrew, Jane, the Parson, and the Fox by Thomas Hardy, from *Tales from Longpuddle*

BOOKWORMS CLUB SILVER
STAGES 2 AND 3

The Christmas Presents by O. Henry, from *New Yorkers*

Netty Sargent and the House by Thomas Hardy, from *Tales from Longpuddle*

Too Old to Rock and Roll by Jan Mark, from *Too Old to Rock and Roll and Other Stories*

A Walk in Amnesia by O. Henry, from *New Yorkers*

The Five Orange Pips by Sir Arthur Conan Doyle, from *Sherlock Holmes Short Stories*

The Tell-Tale Heart by Edgar Allan Poe, from *Tales of Mystery and Imagination*

Go, Lovely Rose by H. E. Bates, from *Go, Lovely Rose and Other Stories*

BOOKWORMS CLUB GOLD
STAGES 3 AND 4

The Black Cat by Edgar Allan Poe, from *Tales of Mystery and Imagination*

Sredni Vashtar by Saki, from *Tooth and Claw*

The Railway Crossing by Freeman Wills Crofts, from *As the Inspector Said and Other Stories*

The Daffodil Sky by H. E. Bates, from *Go, Lovely Rose and Other Stories*

A Moment of Madness by Thomas Hardy, from *The Three Strangers and Other Stories*

The Secret by Arthur C. Clarke, from *The Songs of Distant Earth and Other Stories*

The Experiment by M. R. James, from *The Unquiet Grave*

BOOKWORMS CLUB DIAMOND
STAGES 5 AND 6

Millie by Katherine Mansfield, from *The Garden Party and Other Stories*

Her First Ball by Katherine Mansfield, from *The Garden Party and Other Stories*

Men and Women by Claire Keegan, from *Treading on Dreams: Stories from Ireland*

Mr Sing My Heart's Delight by Brian Friel, from *Treading on Dreams: Stories from Ireland*

Death Wish by Lawrence Block, from *American Crime Stories*

Cooking the Books by Christopher Fowler, from *The Fly and Other Horror Stories*

The Stolen Body by H. G. Wells, from *The Fly and Other Horror Stories*

ROLE BADGES

These role icons can be photocopied and then cut out to make badges or stickers for the members of the Reading Circle to wear.